D1066359

ENERGY CHANGES
IN BIOCHEMICAL REACTIONS

ENERGY CHANGES
IN BIOCHEMICAL REACTIONS

IRVING M. KLOTZ

DEPARTMENT OF CHEMISTRY
NORTHWESTERN UNIVERSITY
EVANSTON, ILLINOIS

1967

ACADEMIC PRESS · New York · London

COPYRIGHT © 1967, BY ACADEMIC PRESS INC.
ALL RIGHTS RESERVED.
NO PART OF THIS BOOK MAY BE REPRODUCED IN ANY FORM,
BY PHOTOSTAT, MICROFILM, OR ANY OTHER MEANS, WITHOUT
WRITTEN PERMISSION FROM THE PUBLISHERS.

ACADEMIC PRESS INC.
111 Fifth Avenue, New York, New York 10003

United Kingdom Edition published by
ACADEMIC PRESS INC. (LONDON) LTD.
Berkeley Square House, London W.1

LIBRARY OF CONGRESS CATALOG CARD NUMBER: 66-30088

Second Printing, 1967

PRINTED IN THE UNITED STATES OF AMERICA

577. QD
K892 501
.K7557

"A theory is the more impressive the greater is the simplicity of its premises, the more different are the kinds of things it relates and the more extended is its range of applicability. Therefore, the deep impression which classical thermodynamics made upon me. It is the only physical theory of universal content which I am convinced, that within the framework of applicability of its basic concepts, will never be overthrown."

A. Einstein

232286

"With the increasing tendency to interpret biological phenomena in molecular terms, many biologists have become anxious to understand the principles of energetics which govern biochemical changes. Nevertheless, they have been understandably reluctant to devote the large amount of time that would be required even to peruse only a standard textbook in this field and to acquire the mathematical background upon which the logical development in such texts is based. However, for many purposes a 'reading knowledge' of the language of thermodynamics may suffice, and this can be acquired without a large expenditure of time. With such knowledge one can at least understand the acknowledged classics in the field; some readers may even be stimulated to acquire the background to apply the concepts of energetics to branches of biology hitherto uninfluenced by these ideas."

This paragraph stated the essence of the philosophy of the first version of this small monograph. In the intervening ten years, the training of students in the sciences has become more intensive and quantitative so that even those at elementary levels are being introduced to concepts and some computations that were reserved for graduate work in chemistry about a generation or two ago. While retaining the original philosophy of this book, I have added several sections devoted to quantitative calculations. Thus I hope that a reader who has conscientiously worked his way through this volume will acquire not only a cocktail-party knowledge of thermodynamics but will be able to apply it to some simple biochemical or chemical reactions.

No doubt some astute reviewer will list a variety of topics not present in this small volume, or will point out that certain subjects ought to be treated more profoundly, and in fact are so treated in some other text, either of his or mine. Let me anticipate such comments by merely remarking that my sources of revelation are superior to his. What is appropriate for the contents of a small monograph of this type obviously reflects the author's interests, taste, and judgment. Another teacher or investigator might select or emphasize different subjects. I can only hope that my selection will prove suitable for some students interested in acquiring an insight into the fundamental concepts and simple calculations of biochemical energetics.

IRVING M. KLOTZ

Evanston, Illinois
January, 1967

Contents

INTRODUCTION: THE SCOPE OF ENERGETICS

The objective of the field of energetics or thermo-dynamics is to establish the principles and laws which govern material transformations. Historically speaking, the subject was initially developed with a primary focus on the energy transformations which accompany these material changes; hence the name *thermodynamics* was precisely descriptive of this branch of learning. Starting near the end of the nineteenth century, however, the dominant point of view changed to one that emphasized the development and use of energy functions to describe the state of a material system and to prescribe rules that govern transitions from one state to another. The energy functions are thus used as a method of bookkeeping in correlating the behavior of matter; hence the name *energetics* is perhaps more appropriate than *thermodynamics* to describe this field of knowledge.

There have been two general approaches to the field of energetics. The classical, or phenomenological, one is based on purely macroscopic observations and concepts; its fundamental ideas, although often highly abstract, can be reduced to common experience. The statistical-molecular approach, in contrast, assumes in addition that matter consists of discrete particles, molecules, whose behavior follows the laws of mechanics. By appealing to molecular images, the statistical viewpoint provides a more concrete mechanical interpretation for thermodynamic concepts. Being based on a molecular model, statistical thermodynamics can use experimental data to provide information on molecular properties. On the other hand, the classical theory in itself is unable to give any information on molecular characteristics. However, this limitation is in a sense also a virtue, for classical energetics is completely independent of any future changes in our conception of molecules. At least for macroscopic phenomena, classical energetics provides a completed logical framework.

We shall examine the subject of energetics first primarily from the phenomenological viewpoint since this approach requires a less sophisticated mathematical background. Once having grasped the basic principles and techniques, we shall also consider briefly some of the insights which are provided by statistical thermodynamics.

I. THE CONCEPT OF ENERGY: THE FIRST LAW OF THERMODYNAMICS

Historically, the concept of energy first arose in considerations of purely mechanical phenomena. It was recognized early in mechanics that if work were done to lift a weight from one position in the gravitational field to another (Fig. I.1), this work could then be fully recovered.[1] Thus for example, the weight resting on the table top in Fig. I.1, if suitably connected to the weight on the floor at the right-hand side, could lift the latter to the top of the table.[1] Thus one may assign to the first weight on the tabletop a certain "capacity to do work," which is latent in the weight by virtue of its position in the gravitational field. This capacity to do work, in the ideal situation of no friction, has the very special attribute of depending only on the height of the weight above the floor and not on the path taken to bring the weight from the floor to the tabletop. It seems appropriate therefore to assign a special name, *energy,* to this capacity to do work, and perhaps to add the adjective *potential* to the word *energy* to emphasize the latent character of the work capacity in this particular example.

Work expended in causing extension of a spring is also an early example of energy in the mechanical sense. If x (Fig. I.2) represents the extension of a spring at rest, then a certain quantity of work must be exerted upon the

[1] This statement is true strictly only for the limiting case in which there is no friction at any of the mechanical contacts, e.g., between the wheel and its bearing in Fig. I.1. Likewise, it is to be understood that the weight on the left in the figure is a fraction of a milligram heavier than that on the right.

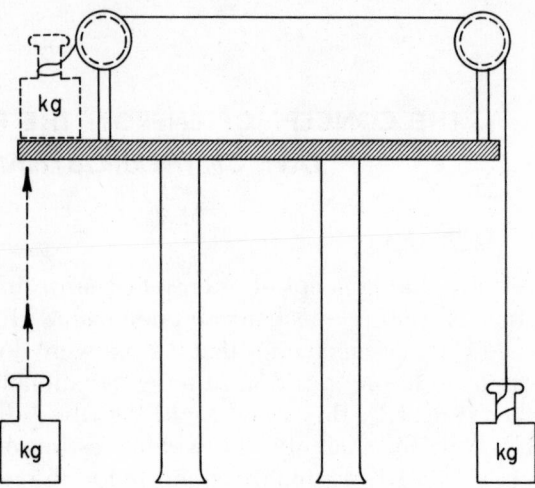

FIG. I.1. Energy and work in a purely mechanical system: a gravitational field.

spring to increase its extension to x'. Again this work may be recovered (fully in ideal circumstances), for example, by attaching the extended spring to a rope and pulley system such as is shown in Fig. I.1 and raising the weight on the right side. Again the capacity of the ideal spring to do work depends only on the distance of extension x', and hence we again may assign the special name *energy* to this capacity to do work.

One might be tempted to generalize from these two examples and think that in all cases where one exerts a force and does some work on a body, the body in its new position retains its capacity to do work. A very familiar

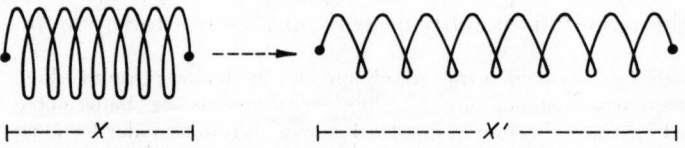

FIG. I.2. Energy and work in a purely mechanical system: a spring.

example would immediately convince us that this generalization cannot be maintained. In Fig. I.1, for example, a substantial amount of work would be required to move the weight along the floor (particularly if the floor were very rough) from the left side to the right side of the table. In this case, the weight on the right does not retain the capacity to do work. In fact one must do work on it to return the weight to its initial position. Clearly in this situation the exertion of work on a body does not result in "giving it energy."

Paralleling historical development, ultimately we recognize an important distinction between our first two experiments and the third. In the last one, where friction is dominant, heat is evolved as the weight is moved along the floor. Since no student approaches this subject without some background in physics, he will at this point immediately say that we could call heat a form of energy. We should recognize first, however, that in doing so we have definitely departed from our initial definition that energy is the capacity to do work. Furthermore, there would be no advantage in making heat comparable to work unless the two were quantitatively interrelated. As every student knows, however, this quantitative equivalence has been demonstrated in the experiments of Joule.

Nevertheless, let us adopt a somewhat more sophisticated view and undertake a more general analysis of the relationships between work, heat, and energy. For this purpose, we may represent merely schematically (Fig. I.3) any one of the many physical or chemical systems with which we shall be concerned. In the special circumstance illustrated, it is assumed that the system does work on the outside, but absorbs heat from the surroundings; alternative circumstances would be represented with arrows pointing in the reverse direction.

As one example of the system represented by Fig. I.3, let us consider a heavy boulder resting on the edge of a steep cliff. This boulder could be brought to the floor of the valley in many ways. One method would be to attach it to one end of a rope, attach another boulder of almost equal weight, resting at the bottom of the valley, to the other end of the rope and by stringing the rope over a pulley wheel suitably mounted at the brink of the cliff, to allow the high boulder to be lowered to the ground

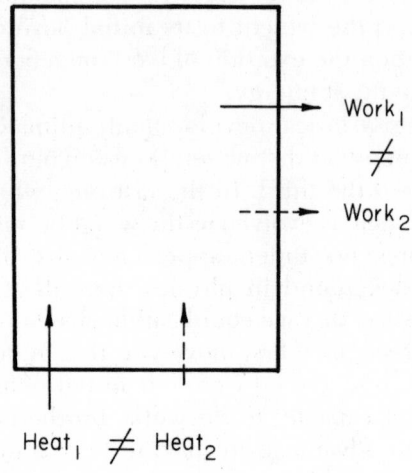

Nevertheless:

$$\text{Heat}_1 - \text{Work}_1 = \text{Heat}_2 - \text{Work}_2$$

FIG. I.3. Relationships between work and heat according to the first law of thermodynamics.

while the second boulder is raised to the top of the cliff. In this procedure the first boulder does a positive amount of work, but no heat is absorbed or evolved in the process. Another method for getting the boulder down might be to let it slide down some pathway to the valley. Less work could be obtained by this method, but a definite quantity of heat would be evolved. Many other paths could be chosen differing in the frictional resistance they would offer to the motion of the boulder. For each path, the work W, done may differ from that for any other path, and the heat, Q, evolved will be different. Nevertheless, despite great variations in comparative values of Q and of W, the *difference* $Q - W$, has been found in all experience to be the same, so long as the respective starting points and final points of the boulder's travel are the same for each path.

As another example of Fig. I.3, we might consider a stretched rubber band. The band could be attached to a weight, so that as the band contracts it does some work, W_1. In this process, a certain amount of heat, Q_1, would be absorbed. A second "path" for the return of the stretched rubber band to a shorter length might be to just let it snap back, i.e., to let $W_2 = 0$; in this process, there would be an associated heat effect Q_2, different from Q_1. Once again, though, despite the inequality of W_1 and W_2 or Q_1 and Q_2, the *difference* $Q_1 - W_1$ has been found equal to $Q_2 - W_2$, for a wide variety of different paths, between the same end points.

This special character of the difference $Q - W$ is not limited to mechanical processes. Consider, for example, the chemical reaction

$$\text{Pyruvate} + \text{H}_2 \rightarrow \text{Lactate} \tag{1.1}$$

This reaction can take place in a suitable electrochemical cell so that electrical work is obtained as the reaction proceeds. Under certain ideal conditions the work obtained[2] is 11,440 calories; in this process $-10,200$ calories of heat are adsorbed (i.e., $+10,200$ calories of heat are evolved by the chemicals). Under certain non-ideal conditions, the electrochemical cell may produce 10,000 calories of work; in this process $-11,640$ calories of heat are absorbed (i.e., $+11,640$ calories of heat are evolved by the chemicals in the cell). In contrast, the same chemical reaction can be carried out in a closed vessel without

[2] E. S. G. Barron and A. B. Hastings, *J. Biol. Chem.*, **107**, 567 (1934).

any work being obtained; under these circumstances −21,640 calories of heat are absorbed (i.e., +21,640 calories are evolved). If, following the usual convention, we call Q the heat *absorbed* by the chemical system under consideration and W the work *done* by the system, then we see once again that $Q - W$ is the same for all three methods, or paths, for carrying out the chemical reaction shown in equation (1.1).

We have considered three special cases of the schematic diagram of Fig. I.3. Going much further, we can summarize a vast amount of experience by generalizing the statements we have made for Q, W, and $Q - W$ so far only in our three special examples. In any system we find that although the value of W, the work done by the system, or Q, the heat absorbed by the system, in going from one state to another, varies with the path chosen, the *difference $Q - W$* is invariant and depends only on where we start and where we end. This remarkable characteristic of the difference quantity $Q - W$ may be emphasized by giving it a special name—the change in energy,[3] ΔE, of the system. In terms of a simple equation we may write

$$\Delta E = Q - W \tag{1.2}$$

The essence of the first law represented by equation (1.2) thus may be summarized in two statements. The first defines a new concept, energy, in terms of directly measurable concepts, heat and work. The second declares that the internal energy, so defined, is a thermodynamic property; that is, it depends only on the state of a system and not on the previous history of the system. To repeat, despite the fact that the heat absorbed, Q, and

---

[3] We shall use the symbol E for the internal energy of a system. The first law of thermodynamics permits us to define, however, only changes in energy, $E_2 - E_1$, where E_2 is the energy of the system at the end of a process and E_1 that at the beginning. For $E_2 - E_1$ we shall use the briefer notation ΔE.

the work done, W, in going from one state to another depend on the particular path used in the transformation, the difference in the two quantities, defined as ΔE, is independent of the method by which the change is accomplished.

It is, furthermore, a necessary consequence of these statements that ΔE around a closed path is zero. If the system is ultimately returned to its initial state, there can be no change in its energy, since E depends only on the state of the system, which has not changed in a cyclic process. Despite this fact, the total Q or W for the cyclical process may differ very much from zero.

It should also be noticed that the very definition of the energy concept precludes the possibility of determining absolute values; that is, we have defined only a method of measuring *changes* in internal energy in terms of heat and work quantities. Classical energetics, by itself, is incapable of determining the absolute zero of reference for the energy function. In practice this limitation is not really a handicap, however, since interest is generally focused on chemical and physical *transformations*, and any convenient state may be chosen as the reference point.

II. THE CONCEPT OF ENTROPY

A. The Second Law of Thermodynamics

We shall be interested in the principles of energetics primarily for their ability to tell us whether a particular biochemical (or biophysical) change is feasible under a specified set of conditions. The first law of thermodynamics, however, does not provide us with a criterion for determining when a transformation may occur spontaneously, as a few specific examples will show.

One unfamiliar with energetics is accustomed to thinking that a chemical or physical change may occur spontaneously only if the final state of the system is at a lower level of energy than the initial (i.e., if ΔE is negative). This conclusion is based on thoroughly valid common experience with movements in gravitational fields. We all recognize that a ball tends to fall from a higher to a lower level, not vice versa. For purely mechanical processes, involving no heat exchange, the rule that ΔE must be negative is valid as a criterion of permissible spontaneous change. What is not often realized is that this rule is completely unreliable if applied to all kinds of transformations.

There are spontaneous transformations that occur despite the fact that the internal energy of the system at the end is essentially the same as before the transformation. For example, when a stretched rubber band is released, it snaps back spontaneously; yet ΔE for this process is substantially zero.

There are even processes that can occur spontaneously despite the fact that the internal energy at the end is greater than at the beginning of the transformation (i.e., for which ΔE is positive). These are particularly common among chemical changes. For example, when a free copper ion and a protein molecule (P) are permitted to come in contact with each other, they will spontaneously form a complex compound:

$$P + Cu^{2+} \rightarrow P{-}Cu^{2+} \tag{2.1}$$

Nevertheless for this reaction ΔE is +3 kcal; that is, $P{-}Cu^{2+}$ has 3 kcal more internal energy than separated P and Cu^{2+} particles. An even more familiar example is the ice-water phase transition. At 1°C, (or at any temperature above 0°C) liquid water is in a higher energy state than ice; nevertheless if ice were at 1°C it would spontaneously be transformed to water (Fig. II.1).

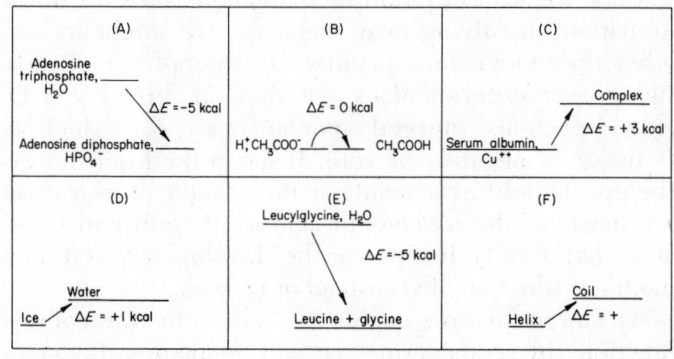

FIG. II.1. Change in energy for some spontaneously occurring chemical transformations.

Thus reactions may occur spontaneously for which ΔE is negative, zero, or positive (Fig. II.1). Clearly ΔE is no criterion of permissibility of a transformation. Apparently the first law of thermodynamics does not contain within it the basis of any criterion of spontaneity. Some further principle will be required to summarize in a general statement the observed tendency of systems of many different types to change in a particular direction.

Let us examine again a process of the type shown in Fig. II.1C, that is, one which proceeds spontaneously to a state of higher energy. At first glance, the occurrence of this transformation might seem to violate the first law, for how can a system spontaneously acquire energy? Actually, of course, this system does not violate the first law; during the spontaneous transformation it absorbs heat (3 kcal in Fig. II.1C) spontaneously from its surroundings.

Evidently, then, some chemical systems are capable of spontaneously absorbing heat from their surroundings in order to proceed to a higher energy state, whereas others are not. Is there any way of telling which systems will behave in each way?

Since ΔE as a criterion of spontaneity fails for transformations involving heat exchange, we might try another thermodynamic quantity, for example Q. Clearly the proper criterion does not depend directly on Q, since reactions proceed spontaneously for which Q is positive, negative or zero. It has turned out, nevertheless, largely as a result of the insight of two great physicists of the nineteenth century, Kelvin and Clausius, that a suitable rule can be developed based on a modified function of Q instead of Q itself.

We can make a reasonable guess as to the form of this function by considering certain analogies between energy in the form of work and energy in the form of heat.

When we analyze in more detail a variety of kinds of work, we find in each case that the total work is determined by two factors, an intensity factor and a capacity factor (Table I). In doing work against gravity, the total work depends on the change in height, h, and also on the mass, m, of the material moved. Electrical work is determined by the voltage drop as well as by the total charge moved by (or against) a particular voltage drop. When a gas expands and does work against a confining piston, the work done depends on the pressure of the gas and also on the volume change during the working expansion.

Insofar as heat energy is concerned (Table I), it is clear that the intensity factor should be the temperature.

TABLE I
INTENSIVE AND EXTENSIVE FACTORS IN FORMS OF ENERGY

	Intensity	Capacity
Work; gravitational	Height, h	Mass, m
Work; stretching	Tension, τ	Length, l
Work; electrical	Voltage, $\mathscr{E}$	Charge, q
Work; expansion	Pressure, P	Volume, V
Work; surface	Surface tension, γ	Area, A
Heat	Temperature, T	?

What, however, should be the corresponding capacity factor?

By a simple dimensional analysis we can see that the quantity Q/T would have at least the proper form:

$$\text{Energy} = \text{Intensity Factor} \times \text{Capacity Factor}$$

$$Q \text{ (calories)} = T \text{ (degrees)} \times \frac{Q \text{ (calories)}}{T \text{ (degrees)}} \qquad (2.2)$$

It would clearly be desirable to see whether this new quantity shows any correspondence with spontaneity in material transformations.

We can summarize a long history of intellectual effort by saying that the new function, if measured in certain prescribed ways, does indeed provide the criterion we have been seeking. The new criterion found may be described as follows. If we wish to know whether a particular system can change spontaneously from one state, a, to another b, then in principle we must evaluate Q/T for a transformation over the same states but carried out in a reversible[1] manner. Furthermore we must also evaluate Q'/T for any changes which would occur in the surroundings during the actual spontaneous transformation. As a result of much experience we know that under natural conditions heat flows spontaneously from a hotter object to a colder one. If we accept this observation as an empirical law of nature, then a remarkable equation can be proved to be *true for any transformation that can occur spontaneously*, to wit:

$$(Q/T)_{\text{system}} + (Q'/T)_{\text{surroundings}} = \text{a positive number} \quad (2.3)$$

For simplicity in notation we may write also

$$\Sigma(Q/T) > 0 \quad\quad\quad (2.4)$$

as the criterion of spontaneity. If

$$\Sigma(Q/T) = 0 \quad\quad\quad (2.5)$$

then the system under consideration is at equilibrium.[2]

As in the case of the quantity $(Q - W)$ discussed in Chapter I, so here the function (Q/T) evidently has very unique characteristics in being able to predict the behavior of physical and chemical systems. It seems appropriate, therefore, to endow it with a special name, change in *entropy*, and to attach to it a special symbol, ΔS. We may replace equations (2.4) and (2.5), therefore, by the following statements, to conform with the forms more commonly found in the scientific literature:

$$\Sigma \Delta S > 0; \text{ spontaneous change possible} \quad (2.6)$$

$$\Sigma \Delta S = 0; \text{ system at equilibrium} \quad\quad (2.7)$$

---

[1] For a discussion of the strict definition of "reversible," see any standard text on thermodynamics.

[2] If $\Sigma(Q/T) < 0$, then for the reverse transformation $\Sigma(Q/T) > 0$. Hence the *reverse* transformation can be spontaneous.

B. Entropy as an Index of Exhaustion

Thus, the second law of thermodynamics provides us with a new function, the entropy change, ΔS, to be used as the fundamental criterion of spontaneity. For a closed region of space including all changes under observation,

$$\Delta S \geqq 0 \qquad (2.8)$$

the equality sign applying to systems at equilibrium, the inequality to all capable of undergoing spontaneous changes.

Spontaneous transformations occur all around us all the time. Hence ΔS, for a section of space encompassing each such transformation and its effect on its surroundings, is a positive number. This realization led Clausius to his famous aphorism,

Die Energie der Welt ist konstant; die
Entropie der Welt strebt einem Maximum zu[3]

To a beginning student this form of statement is probably the source of more perplexity than enlightenment. The constancy of energy causes no difficulty of course. Since energy is conserved, it fits into the category of concepts to which we attribute permanence. In thought one usually pictures energy as a kind of material fluid, and hence even if it flows from one place to another, its conservation may be visualized readily. However, when one carries over an analogous mental picture to the concept of entropy one immediately is faced with the bewildering realization that entropy is being created out of nothing whenever there is an increase in entropy in an isolated system undergoing a spontaneous transformation.

The heart of the difficulty of "understanding" the concept of increase in entropy is a verbal one. It is very

[3] The energy of the universe is constant; the entropy tends toward a maximum.

difficult to dissociate the unconscious verbal implications of a word which we have used all of our lives in other contexts without critical analysis. In speaking of "increase in entropy" we are using language appropriate for the description of material bodies. Automatically, therefore, we associate with entropy other characteristics of material bodies that are at variance with the nature of entropy and hence that are a source of confusion.

Ultimately, one must realize that entropy is essentially a mathematical function. It is a concise function of the variables of experience, e.g., temperature, pressure, and composition. Natural processes tend to occur only in certain directions, that is, the variables pressure, temperature, and composition change only in certain ways, but very complicated ways, which are most concisely described by the change in a single function, the entropy function ($\Delta S > 0$).

Some of the historical reluctance to assimilate the entropy concept into general scientific thinking, and much of the introductory student's bewilderment, might have been avoided if Clausius had defined entropy (as would have been perfectly legitimate to do) as

$$\Sigma \, \Delta S' = \Sigma \, (- \, Q/T) \tag{2.9}$$

with a negative sign instead of the positive one of equation (2.4). With this definition all of the thermodynamic consequences which have been derived from the entropy function would be just as valid except that some relations would change in sign. Thus, in place of equation (2.8) we would find that for an isolated system,

$$\Delta S' \leqq 0 \tag{2.10}$$

the equality sign applying to systems at equilibrium, the inequality to systems capable of spontaneous changes. Now, however, we would recognize that for all isolated sections of space undergoing actual changes, ΔS is a *negative* number; that is, the entropy *decreases*. Likewise, paraphrasing Clausius, we would say, "Die Entropie der Welt strebt einem *Minimum* zu." This statement would accord more obviously with our experience that observable spontaneous changes go in the direction which *decreases* the capacity for further spontaneous change, and that the universe (or at least the solar system) changes in time toward a state in which (ultimately) no further spontaneous change will be possible. We need merely cite a few examples: solutes always diffuse from a more concentrated solution to a dilute one; clocks tend to run down; magnets become self-demagnetized; heat always flows from a warm body to a colder one; gases always effuse into a vacuum; aqueous solutions of $NaCl$ and $AgNO_3$ if mixed always form $AgCl$. Although some of these individual changes can be reversed by some outside agency, this outside agent must itself undergo a transformation which decreases its capacity for further spontaneous change. It is impossible to restore every system back to its original condition. On earth, our ultimate sources of energy for work are the sun, or nuclear power; in either case, these ultimate nuclear reactions proceed unidirectionally and toward the loss of capacity for further spontaneous change.

Thus, we ought to view entropy as an index of condition or character (perhaps somewhat analogous to a cost-of-living index or to pH as an index of acidity) rather than as a measure of content of some imaginary fluid. It is an index of the capacity for spontaneous change. By historical accident the index was actually defined so that it *increases* as the capacity of an isolated system for spontaneous change *decreases*.[4] In other words, the more a system exhausts its capacity for spontaneous change, the larger the entropy index. Hence

---

[4] In an analogous fashion, the index of acidity, pH, *increases* as the H^+ concentration or actual acidity *decreases*.

we should preferably say that *entropy is an index of exhaustion;* the more a system has lost its capacity for spontaneous change, the more this capacity has been exhausted, the greater is the entropy.

In some respects, especially pedagogical ones, it might have been better to change the sign of the original definition of the index so that it would measure residual capacity rather than loss of capacity. However, with the development of molecular-statistical energetics (see Chapter VIII) and the identification of entropy (in terms of kinetic-molecular theory) with the degree of disorder of a system, the original sign chosen by Clausius turns out to be the more convenient one. The universal tendency of all changes to reduce everything to a state of equilibrium may be correlated with the rearrangements of molecules from orderly to disorderly configurations. And since there are more disorderly arrangements than orderly ones, it is appropriate that the entropy index increase with the approach of all things to a state of equilibrium.

III. THE FREE ENERGY OR CHEMICAL POTENTIAL

A. A Criterion of Feasibility of a Material Transformation

In principle, the second law of thermodynamics summarizes our experience, in terms of the properties of the entropy function, as regards the conditions under which a transformation can take place spontaneously. In practice, however, this function is not a convenient one to use. It requires us to evaluate the changes in entropy both in the changing substance and in its surroundings, in other words, in a section of space large enough to include all changes caused by the reaction. It would be much more convenient if we could restrict our attention merely to the material transformation itself, whose environment we can generally control, without paying any attention to changes in properties of the surroundings. Furthermore, it would be desirable to have a criterion of feasibility applicable under conditions normally characteristic of biological reactions: (1) constant pressure, usually that of the atmosphere; and (2) constant temperature.

These objectives were accomplished by Gibbs and by Helmholtz who created the *free energy function* by fusing the first and the second laws into a single mathematical statement (Fig. III.1). Thus, it was recognized that the law of conservation of energy requires that

$$(Q'/T)_{\text{surroundings}} \equiv \Delta S_{\text{surroundings}}$$
$$= -\Delta(E + PV)_{\text{system}}/T \quad (3.1)$$

where P and V are the pressure on and the volume of the system, respectively. Substitution of this expression into equations (2.3)–(2.7), followed by simple algebraic manipulation, leads to the following rule for a system at constant pressure and temperature:

$$\Delta E_{\text{system}} + P\,\Delta V_{\text{system}} - T\,\Delta S_{\text{system}} \lesseqgtr 0 \qquad (3.2)$$

The inequality sign applies to any spontaneous change and the zero to any system at equilibrium. Now that each

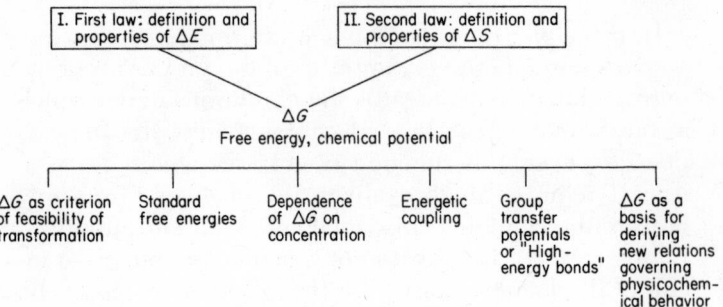

FIG. III.1. Logical relationships in energetics.

thermodynamic quantity in the criterion of feasibility refers to the system itself, and the properties of the surroundings have been excised, we can omit the subscripts in equation (3.2). Furthermore, for conciseness we create a new function, G,[1] and name, *Gibbs free energy*, defined so that equation (3.2) may be replaced by

$$\Delta E + P\,\Delta V - T\,\Delta S = \Delta G \lesseqgtr 0 \qquad (3.3)$$

Thus, the free energy change for a specified reaction may be negative, in which case the reaction can proceed spontaneously, or zero, in which case the substances are at equilibrium.[2] Of course ΔG could turn out to be a posi-

[1] The letter F has also been commonly used for the Gibbs energy, particularly in the United States. Most tabulations of chemical thermodynamic data use F (and hence ΔF).

[2] At constant pressure and temperature, G (or ΔG) depends only on the composition of the system and not on its history. This feature, plus its fundamental character of being a criterion of feasibility, makes the name "chemical *potential*" particularly appropriate.

tive number, but in this case the exactly opposite reaction is accompanied by a negative ΔG and, therefore, this opposite reaction can proceed spontaneously.

In classical energetics the first and second terms on the left-hand side of equation (3.3) are combined into another quantity, ΔH, called the change in enthalpy. Thus an equivalent form of equation (3.3) is

$$\Delta G = \Delta H - T \Delta S \tag{3.4}$$

For our purposes, however, it will usually not be necessary to consider the distinction between ΔH and ΔE. For most reactions which occur in solution, especially those of biological interest, the $P \Delta V$ term makes a negligible contribution to the energetics because the volume change, ΔV, during the course of the transformation is very small. Hence for most practical purposes ΔH and ΔE will be indistinguishable in situations of primary interest to us, and thus we may write

$$\Delta G \cong \Delta E - T \Delta S \tag{3.5}$$

As is evident from equation (3.5) the sign and size of ΔG will reflect contributions from both the change in internal energy and the change in entropy during the transformation. It is easy enough to accept the conclusion that if the internal energy of a system drops, i.e., if ΔE is negative, then ΔG should be negative, and the free energy drop should be available for useful work. However, it is not so simple to see at this point, since there exists no mechanical analogy, that even if ΔE were zero, ΔG could still be negative and useful work could be obtained; such is the case when ΔS is a positive number for a particular transformation. We shall consider in a later chapter some molecular properties related to ΔS and thereby obtain a greater insight into the significance of entropy changes. For the moment, let us merely examine one simple specific example of the counterplay of the ΔE and ΔS factors.

Liquid water may be converted to ice at different temperatures:

$$H_2O \text{ (l)} = H_2O \text{ (s)} \tag{3.6}$$

The changes in thermodynamic properties for this transformation are known in the temperature range slightly below and slightly above 0°C. These may be summarized in the following table:

Temperature (°C)	ΔE (cal mole^{-1})	ΔH (cal mole^{-1})	ΔS (cal mole^{-1} deg^{-1})	$-T \Delta S$ (cal mole^{-1})	ΔG (cal mole^{-1})
−10	−1343	−1343	−4.9	1292	−51
0	−1436	−1436	−5.2	1436	0
+10	−1529	−1529	−5.6	1583	+54

We note first that at each temperature there is a *drop* in energy as we go from the liquid to the solid, and on this basis alone, water should spontaneously freeze at all temperatures between −10 and +10°C. In fact the drop in energy is greatest at +10°C, and one might even expect the liquid to freeze most readily at this temperature, whereas actually it cannot do so at all. The counterbalancing factor is the entropy, which is negative at each temperature, and increasingly so as the temperature rises. (As we shall see in Chapter VIII, a decrease in entropy is associated with a transformation to a more orderly state, and of course in this example it is obvious that crystalline ice contains a more orderly arrangement of molecules than does liquid water.) At −10°, ΔS, when multiplied by T, contributes +1292 cal; this being numerically less than the ΔH (or ΔE) of −1343, we arrive at a net ΔG of −51 cal mole^{-1}, and hence conclude that the transformation can occur spontaneously. At 0°C, ΔH (or ΔE) and $T \Delta S$ balance exactly and ΔG is zero; thus the system is at equilibrium. As the temperature increases further, however, $-T \Delta S$ increases more rapidly than ΔH (or ΔE) drops, the net ΔG becomes a positive number, and we conclude that the *reverse* reaction (ice → water) must be the spontaneous one.

B. Distinction between $\Delta G°$ and ΔG

We now have in the free energy function, ΔG, a convenient fusion of the first and second laws which provides a quantitative indication of the potential ability of a substance to undergo a chemical or physical transformation. Before embarking on some actual numerical computations, however, it is advisable to clarify one additional feature of ΔG. Merely specifying the nature of the chemical change does not lead to a specific value for ΔG; the magnitude depends also on the conditions under which the reaction is carried out.

For example, let us consider the synthesis of the following peptide bond from aqueous solutions of alanine (Ala) and glycine (Gly):

$$\text{Ala (aq)} + \text{Gly (aq)} = \text{Ala—Gly (aq)} + H_2O \text{ (l)} \quad (3.7)$$

If the reaction occurs at the concentrations:

$$1 \, M \qquad 1 \, M \qquad 1 \, M; \qquad \Delta G° = 4130 \text{ cal mole}^{-1}$$

These conditions, as we shall see later are defined as *standard conditions*, and therefore the ΔG for this special situation is labeled $\Delta G°$ and called the *standard* free energy change. Turning to some other conditions, we might pick the concentrations:

$$0.1 \, M \qquad 0.1 \, M \qquad 1.25 \times 10^{-5} \, M; \qquad \Delta G = 0$$

These concentrations happen to be one set at which this reaction is at equilibrium; therefore ΔG is zero. Another set of concentrations, neither all standard, nor equilibrium values, is:

$$1 \, M \qquad 1 \, M \qquad 0.1 \, M; \qquad \Delta G = 2700 \text{ cal mole}^{-1}$$

The free energy change for this system, whose calculation depends on steps to be outlined in Chapter V, is neither $\Delta G°$ nor zero.

Thus ΔG depends on the states of the reactants and products, as well as on the nature of the transformation. To illustrate methods of computation, therefore, we shall divide our exposition into two sections. In the first we shall consider only methods of calculating standard free energies, $\Delta G°$. Thereafter we shall proceed to outline methods used to calculate ΔG accompanying changes in concentration, or state, and in this way cover a full range of conditions of biochemical interest.

IV. COMPUTATIONS OF STANDARD FREE ENERGIES

There are a number of general procedures for calculating $\Delta G°$. In any specific instance, the one chosen depends on the data available. A few typical examples will illustrate some useful procedures.

A. From Equilibrium Constants

If equilibrium data are available, the standard free energy change for the reaction may be computed directly from the relation

$$\Delta G° = - RT \ln K \qquad (4.1)$$

where R is the gas law constant (1.987 cal mole^{-1} deg^{-1}) and K the equilibrium constant. Equation (4.1) will be accepted without proof, but it can be derived readily once one knows the relationship between free energy (or chemical potential) and concentration.[1]

As a specific numerical example of such a calculation, let us consider the following step in glycogen metabolism:

$$\text{Glucose 1-phosphate} = \text{Glucose 6-phosphate} \qquad (4.2)$$

This conversion is catalyzed by the enzyme phosphoglucomutase. The equilibrium has been studied extensively[2]; at 25° and pH 7, K is 17. Therefore,

$$\begin{aligned} \Delta G° &= - (1.987)(298.15)(2.303)(\ln 17) \qquad (4.3) \\ &= -1700 \text{ cal mole}^{-1} \end{aligned}$$

[1] See for example, I. M. Klotz, *Chemical Thermodynamics*, Revised Edition, W. A. Benjamin, Inc., New York, 1964, pp. 154-5, 358-9.

[2] See for example, M. R. Atkinson, E. Johnson and R. K. Morton, *Biochem. J.*, **79**, 12 (1961).

Thus the transphosphorylation will occur spontaneously under *standard conditions*.

It might be appropriate at this juncture to emphasize an important and somewhat subtle point. Although we use equilibrium data to obtain the value of K inserted into equation (4.1), or (4.3), the free energy change computed is *not* for the transformation under equilibrium conditions. Quite the contrary, the ΔG obtained is $\Delta G°$, for *standard* conditions. Why this should be so is only apparent in an examination of the derivation of equation (4.1), which we have omitted. Nevertheless, it is a fact that from measurements on the equilibrium state, we can compute a free energy change for the *non*equilibrium state. In this connection, we should recall that ΔG is zero for a reaction at equilibrium.

Let us also examine another specific example of a $\Delta G°$ calculation in which we will penetrate a little further to the actual experimental measurements. A subject of long interest to protein biochemists is the thermodynamics of protein denaturation. One system that has been studied extensively in different ways is chymotrypsinogen. If its denaturation is reversible and is simply a two-state transition, we may represent the reaction

$$N \text{ (native)} = D \text{ (denatured)} \qquad (4.4)$$

by an equilibrium constant, K

$$K = \frac{[D]}{[N]} \qquad (4.5)$$

If this equilibrium constant could be evaluated, we could immediately compute $\Delta G°$ for denaturation from equation (4.1).

Proteins undergo changes in absorption of ultraviolet light when they are denatured. Such changes may be used, therefore, to follow the extent of denaturation. If heat is used to denature chymotrypsinogen at some specified pH, one finds a sigmoid-type change in ultra-violet difference spectrum[3] as is illustrated by any one of the curves in Fig. IV.1. The difference extinction co-efficient, $\Delta\epsilon_N$, at 293 mμ, for the fully native protein increases slightly with temperature, as does that, $\Delta\epsilon_D$, for the fully denatured chymotrypsinogen. These small changes are shown by the hatched lines in Fig. IV.1.

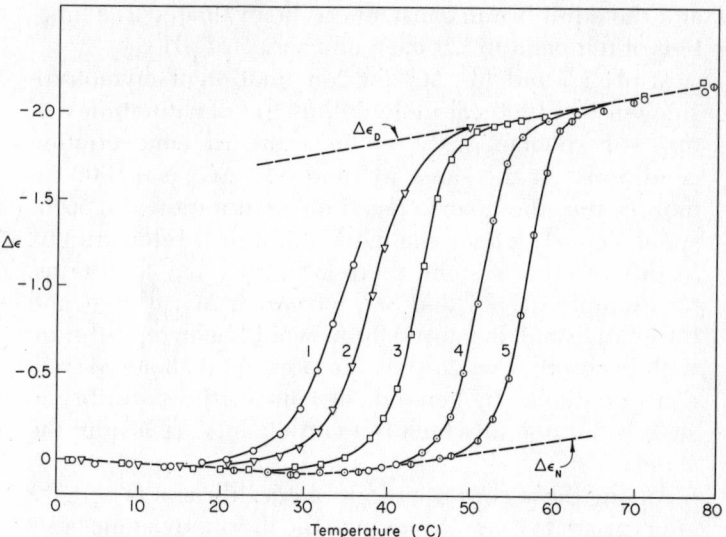

FIG. IV.1. Variation of $\Delta\epsilon_{293m\mu}$ with temperature at pH's 1.11 (curve 1), 1.71 (curve 2), 2.07 (curve 3), 2.56 (curve 4), and 3.00 (curve 5).

Major changes in extinction occur when N → D. For example, curve 3 in Fig. IV.1 shows a sharp rise as the temperature goes above 40°, as the native protein is converted more and more to the denatured form. The closer we approach the line for $\Delta\epsilon_D$, the more nearly complete is the denaturation. At some intermediate temperature, for example, between 40° and 50° in curve 3, we have a mixture of N and D, with an extinction coefficient $\Delta\epsilon$. It

[3] J. F. Brandts, *J. Am. Chem. Soc.*, **86**, 4291 (1964).

is reasonable to assume[4] that $\Delta\epsilon - \Delta\epsilon_N$, the distance upward to the denatured form should be proportional to the concentration of (D), and that the remaining distance $\Delta\epsilon_D - \Delta\epsilon$ should be proportional to (N). Thus we may write

$$K = \frac{\Delta\epsilon - \Delta\epsilon_N}{\Delta\epsilon_D - \Delta\epsilon} \tag{4.6}$$

and the equilibrium constant can be evaluated as a function of temperature, at each of a series of pH's.

At pH 1.7 and 43°, $\Delta G°$ for denaturation of chymotrypsinogen is -1000 cal mole^{-1}; thus the denaturation will proceed spontaneously under standard concentration conditions. At the same pH and 34°, $\Delta G°$ is $+1000$ cal mole^{-1}; thus the reverse reaction, renaturation will occur spontaneously under standard conditions. Interestingly, in this reacting system, there are also some conditions, for example pH 1.7 and 38°, for which $\Delta G°$ is zero, and thus native and denatured forms would be in equilibrium with each other when they are present at standard state concentrations. In general, of course, the equilibrium state is *not* one in which the participants are also in the standard state.

Among these considerations of equilibria, it is perhaps appropriate to draw attention to the thermodynamic basis of one of the fundamental principles of chemical transformations: an enzyme or catalyst cannot shift the equilibrium point. This statement is an automatic consequence of equation (4.1). If an enzyme were to shift an equilibrium in one direction, without itself undergoing any alteration in state, then K_{equil} would acquire a new value. Consequently $\Delta G°$ would differ in the presence of enzyme. But $\Delta G°$ refers to the change in free energy under specific, standard conditions, the same in the presence or absence of enzyme. Since standard condi-

---

[4] This assumption can be shown to be rigorously valid if the absorptions of the two species follow Beer's law.

tions are the same whether catalyst is present or not, ΔG° can have only a single value. The chemical potential, G, like other thermodynamic properties, such as internal energy, E, or entropy, S, depends only on the state of the system. In a change of state, ΔG depends only on the initial and final states, not on the physical or chemical path traversed to achieve this change. From these considerations it follows that ΔG° must have the same value in the presence or absence of a catalyst, and hence that an equilibrium constant cannot be shifted upon introduction of an enzyme.

In essence, what we are saying is that if an enzyme shifted an equilibrium, we should violate the laws of thermodynamics. A more impressive statement might be one which points out that if an enzyme affected an equilibrium, we could construct a perpetual motion machine. Consider for example a reaction

$$A + B = C + D + E$$

in which the volumes of the substances on the right are greater than those on the left. Let us assume for ease in visualization that A, B, C, D, and E are all gases. We allow these substances to reach equilibrium, in the absence of enzyme, in a vessel of the form shown in Fig.

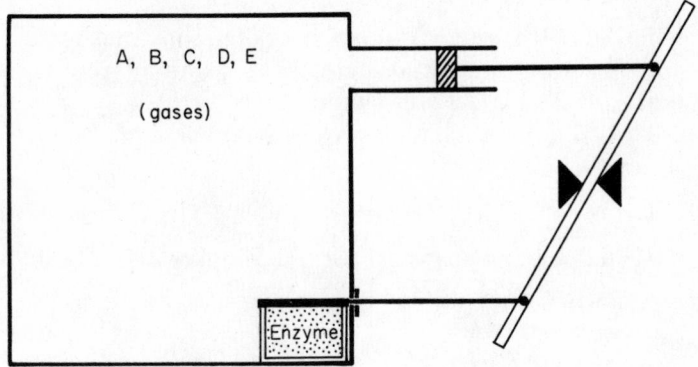

FIG. IV.2. Alleged perpetual motion machine.

IV.2. The enzyme is held in a closed container at one corner of the large vessel. Once equilibrium is attained in the absence of enzyme, we slide the cover of the container over to a position which exposes the gases to the enzyme. If the enzyme affected the equilibrium—for example, shifted it to the right—the volume of the system would increase and the piston would be pushed out. By a simple arrangement of rods and levers attached to the piston, we could use a small part of the expansion force to slide back the cover of the enzyme container. The gases would then return to their initial equilibrium, the volume would decrease and the piston would move in.[5] As the piston moved in, the enzyme would become uncovered, and the cycle would be started again. This sequence of operations would recycle indefinitely. Thus, if an enzyme affected an equilibrium, we could construct a perpetual motion machine.

B. From Oxidation-Reduction Potentials

Tables of standard oxidation-reduction potentials, $\mathscr{E}°$, are available[6] for many substances of biochemical interest. The relationship for converting this information to $\Delta G°$ is

$$\Delta G° = -n\mathscr{F}\mathscr{E}° \tag{4.7}$$

where n is the number of moles of electrons transferred and $\mathscr{F}$ is the Faraday constant, 96,487 coulombs equivalent^{-1}, or 23,061 cal volt^{-1} equiv^{-1}.

Thus if we ask whether ferrocytochrome c can reduce ferricytochrome f,

$$\text{Cyt c Fe}^{\text{II}} + \text{Cyt f Fe}^{\text{III}} = \text{Cyt c Fe}^{\text{III}} + \text{Cyt f Fe}^{\text{II}} \tag{4.8}$$

we can obtain an answer if we can compute $\Delta G°$. For this

[5] The same net effect would be obtained if the enzyme shifted the equilibrium to the left.

[6] W. M. Clark, *Oxidation-Reduction Potentials of Organic Systems*, Williams and Wilkins Co., Baltimore, 1960.

reaction at pH 7, $\mathscr{E}°$ is 0.11 volt. Therefore,

$$\begin{aligned} \Delta G° &= -(1)(23,061)(0.11) \\ &= -2540 \text{ cal mole}^{-1} \end{aligned} \qquad (4.9)$$

and the electron transfer can occur spontaneously.

C. From Enthalpy and Entropy Changes

A third approach to the calculation of free energy changes starts with the equation [see equation (3.4)]

$$\Delta G° = \Delta H° - T \Delta S° \qquad (4.10)$$

If the enthalpy change, $\Delta H°$, and the entropy change, $\Delta S°$, for the reaction can be calculated, then $\Delta G°$ can be obtained promptly.

Generally, authoritative sources[7] list $\Delta H f°$, the standard enthalpy of formation of a substance from its elements at the same temperature. It can be shown by simple algebra that for any reaction,

$$\Delta H° = \Delta H f°_{\text{products}} - \Delta H f°_{\text{reactants}} \qquad (4.11)$$

Similarly, authoritative tables[7] frequently have values of $S_T°$, the absolute entropy of a substance at the temperature T. It is obvious that for any reaction

$$\Delta S° = S°_{\text{products}} - S°_{\text{reactants}} \qquad (4.12)$$

Let us apply these simple rules to a sample calculation. For each of the components of the reaction in the synthesis of (solid) leucyl-glycine we can find $\Delta H f°$ and $S°$ (Table IV.1). These can be listed conveniently below each substance in the equation for the reaction

	DL-Leu (s) +	Gly (s)	= Leu-Gly (s) +	H_2O (l)	(4.13)
$\Delta H f°$:	$-154,160$	$-126,660$	$-207,100$	$-68,317$	
$S°$:	49.5	26.1	67.2	16.716	

[7] *Selected Values of Chemical Thermodynamic Properties,* Nat. Bur. Standards (U. S.), Circ. 500, 1952; *Selected Values of Properties of Chemical Compounds,* Manufacturing Chemists Association, Carnegie Institute of Technology, Pittsburgh, 1955.

where (s) represents the solid state and (l) the liquid. Thus for this reaction,

$$\Delta H° = -207{,}100 - 68{,}317 - (-154{,}160 - 126{,}660)$$
$$= 5400 \text{ cal mole}^{-1}$$
$$\Delta S° = 67.2 + 16.716 - (49.5 + 26.1)$$
$$= 8.3 \text{ cal mole}^{-1} \text{ deg}^{-1}$$
$$\Delta G° = 5400 - (298)(8.3) = 2920 \text{ cal mole}^{-1}$$

Another example will illustrate the use of equation (4.10) together with a corollary principle of energetics. For instance, the hydrolysis of cytidine 2′,3′-cyclic phosphate has been studied widely, since this compound is a very convenient substrate for pancreatic ribonuclease. It would be desirable to know $\Delta G°$ for this hydrolysis. It is a relatively straightforward matter to obtain calorimetric measurements directly for the reaction of interest:

Cytidine 2′,3′-cyclic phosphate (aq) + H_2O (l) $\xrightarrow{\Delta H°}$

Cytidine 3′-phosphate (aq)   (4.14)

However it is not feasible to obtain $\Delta S°$ directly for this reaction. On the other hand it is possible to evaluate $\Delta S°$'s for a series of steps which start with the same reactants and which end with the same products as are shown in equation (4.14) but which involve a different reaction pathway:

Cytidine 2′,3′-cyclic   Cytidine 3′-phosphate (aq)
  phosphate (aq) + H_2O (l)
        $\downarrow \Delta S_1°$ $\uparrow \Delta S_3°$ (4.15)
Cytidine 2′,3′-cyclic $\xrightarrow{\Delta S_2°}$ Cytidine 3′-phosphate (s)
  phosphate (s) + H_2O (l)

As mentioned earlier in regard to the free energy, the laws of thermodynamics also require that

$$\Delta S_1° + \Delta S_2° + \Delta S_3° = \Delta S° \text{ for (4.14)} \qquad (4.16)$$

because the pathway used in going from reactants to products is irrelevant insofar as values of the thermo-

TABLE IV.1

HEATS OF FORMATION, $\Delta Hf°$, AND ABSOLUTE ENTROPIES,
$S°$ AT 25°C FOR SUBSTANCES IN THE SOLID STATE

Substance	$\Delta Hf°$ (kcal mole^{-1})	$S°$ (cal mole^{-1} deg^{-1})
L-Alanine	−134.60	31.6
DL-Alanine	−135.19	31.6
L-Asparagine	−189.36	41.7
L-Aspartic acid	−233.33	41.5
L-Cysteine	−127.88	40.6
L-Cystine	−251.92	68.5
Glycine	−126.66	26.1
L-Glutamic acid	−241.16	45.7
Hippuric acid	−147.71	57.1
L-Leucine	−153.39	49.5
D-Leucine	−153.36	49.5
DL-Leucine	−154.16	49.5
DL-Leucylglycine	−207.10	67.2
L-Tyrosine	−165.43	53.0
CO_2 (g)	−94.0518	51.08
H_2O (l)	−68.3174	16.716

dynamic properties are concerned. Thus it is possible to compute $\Delta G°$ for equation (4.14). Specifically, the values of the thermodynamic quantities at 25° are[8]

$$\Delta S_1° = +8.22 \text{ cal mole}^{-1} \text{ deg}^{-1}$$
$$\Delta S_2° = -9.9 \text{ cal mole}^{-1} \text{ deg}^{-1}$$
$$\Delta S_3° = +8.28 \text{ cal mole}^{-1} \text{ deg}^{-1}$$
$$\Delta S° = 6.6 \text{ cal mole}^{-1} \text{ deg}^{-1} \tag{4.17}$$

$$\Delta H° = -2800 \text{ cal mole}^{-1}$$
$$\Delta G° = -4800 \text{ cal mole}^{-1}$$

The negative value of $\Delta G°$ corresponds with the known fact that cytidine cyclic phosphate will hydrolyze spontaneously in the presence of the enzyme ribonuclease.

[8] J. T. Bahr, R. E. Cathou and G. G. Hammes, *J. Biol. Chem.*, **240**, 3372 (1965).

D. From Free Energies of Formation

Thermodynamic data have now been accumulated for many substances involved in metabolic and biosynthetic processes. One concise way of summarizing this information is in terms of $\Delta Gf°$, the standard free energy of formation of the substance from the elements. A list of $\Delta Gf°$'s is presented in Table IV.2.

TABLE IV.2

STANDARD FREE ENERGIES OF FORMATION, $\Delta Gf°$, AT 25°C

Substance	$\Delta Gf°$ (kcal mole^{-1})	
	Pure solid	In aqueous solution
Acetic acid (l)	−93.75	−95.48
Acetate ion	–	−88.99
cis-Aconitate^{3-}	–	−220.51
L-Alanine	−88.40	−88.75
DL-Alanine	–	−89.11
DL-Alanylglycine	–	−114.57
NH$_3$ (gas)	−3.98	−6.37
NH$_4^+$ ion	–	−19.00
L-Aspartic acid	−174.76	−172.31
L-Aspartate$^-$	–	−166.99
Carbon (graphite)	0.00	–
CO$_2$ (gas)	−94.26	−92.31
HCO$_3^-$	–	−140.31
Citrate^{3-}	–	−279.24
Creatine	–	−63.17
Creatinine	–	−6.91
Cystine	−163.55	−159.00
Cysteine	−82.08	−81.21
Ethanol (l)	−41.77	−43.39
Fructose	–	−218.78
Fumaric acid	−156.49	−154.67
Fumarate^{2-}	–	−144.41
α-D-Galactose	−220.00	−220.73
α-D-Glucose	−217.56	−219.22
L-Glutamate$^-$	–	−165.87
Glycerol (l)	−114.02	−116.76

TABLE IV.2 (*Continued*)

| Substance | ΔGf° (kcal mole^{-1}) | |
	Pure solid	In aqueous solution
Glycine	−88.61	−89.14
Glycogen (per glucose unit)	–	−158.3
OH$^-$ ion	–	−37.60
Hydrogen (gas)	0.00	–
H$^+$ ion	–	0.00
α-Ketoglutarate^{2-}	–	−190.62
Lactate$^-$	–	−123.76
α-Lactose	–	−362.15
β-Lactose	–	−375.26
L-Leucine	−82.63	−81.68
DL-Leucine	–	−81.76
DL-Leucylglycine	–	−110.90
Malate^{2-}	–	−201.98
β-Maltose	–	−357.80
Nitrogen (gas)	0.00	–
Oxalacetate^{2-}	–	−190.53
Oxygen (gas)	0.00	–
Pyruvate$^-$	–	−113.44
Succinic acid	−178.68	−178.39
Succinate^{2-}	–	−164.97
Sucrose	−369.20	−370.90
Urea	−47.12	−48.72
Water (l)	−56.69	–

We may illustrate the use of such a table with the following simple problem. Suppose we wish to find ΔG° for the racemization of L-alanine:

$$\text{L-Ala (aq)} = \text{DL-Ala (aq)} \qquad (4.18)$$

From the listing in Table IV.2, it follows that for the formation of DL-Ala from its elements,

$$3\text{C (graphite)} + 3\tfrac{1}{2}\text{H}_2 \text{ (g)} + \text{O}_2 \text{ (g)} + \tfrac{1}{2}\text{N (g)}$$
$$= \text{DL-Ala (aq)};$$
$$\Delta G^\circ = \Delta Gf^\circ \text{ (DL-Ala)}$$
$$= -89{,}110 \text{ cal mole}^{-1} \qquad (4.19)$$

Correspondingly, for the reverse reaction for L-Ala,

$$\text{L-Ala (aq)} = 3C \text{ (graphite)} + 3\tfrac{1}{2}H_2 \text{ (g)} + O_2 \text{ (g)} + \tfrac{1}{2}N_2 \text{ (g)};$$
$$\Delta G^\circ = -\Delta Gf^\circ \text{ (L-Ala)}$$
$$= +88{,}759 \text{ cal mole}^{-1} \quad (4.20)$$

Addition of equations (4.19) and (4.20) leads to:

$$\text{L-Ala (aq)} = \text{DL-Ala (aq)}; \quad \Delta G^\circ = -360 \text{ cal mole}^{-1}$$

Thus racemization could occur spontaneously; but thermodynamics says nothing about the rate of the reaction.

With this example we conclude our survey of methods for the computation of *standard* free energies. Now we must turn our attention to nonstandard conditions.

Exercises

I. Using the table of free energies of formation, find ΔG° for the reaction

$$\text{Glucose (aq)} + O_2 \text{ (g)}$$
$$= 2\text{Pyruvate}^{-1} \text{ (aq)} + 2H^+ \text{ (aq)} + 2H_2O \text{ (l)}$$

Answer: -121.04 kcal mole^{-1}

II. Can the dehydration of malate to fumarate (in the Krebs cycle) occur spontaneously?

Answer: $\Delta G^\circ = 0.88$ kcal mole^{-1}

III. The equilibrium constant for the reaction

$$\text{Ala (aq)} + \text{Gly (aq)} = \text{Ala-Gly (aq)} + H_2O$$

is 1.25×10^{-3} at 38°C. Assuming that the equilibrium constant is essentially the same at 25°C and using a table of ΔGf°'s for L-alanine and glycine, find the standard free energy of formation of alanylglycine in aqueous solution.

V. THE DEPENDENCE OF CHEMICAL POTENTIAL ON CONCENTRATION

Once we know $\Delta G°$, we could calculate ΔG for any other set of conditions if we knew how to obtain the change in free energy as we change the state of each participant in the reaction. The solution of the last step becomes straightforward once we set forth the fundamental relationship between chemical potential (free energy) and concentration.

A. Fundamental Relationship

The basic statement relates free energy, G, to a "generalized concentration," a, which is actually called the *activity:*

$$G = RT \ln a + \text{constant} \qquad (5.1)$$

We shall discuss, in a moment, the manner in which activity is reduced to experimentally measured concentrations. At this point let us first apply equation (5.1) to the problem of calculating ΔG for the process of changing the state of any substance A from one condition to another:

$$A\,(\text{conc}) = A\,(\text{conc}') \qquad (5.2)$$

It follows from equation (5.1) that ΔG for the reaction in equation (5.2) is given by

$$\Delta G = G' - G = RT \ln a' - RT \ln a = RT \ln a'/a \qquad (5.3)$$

To make actual computations, we now need to specify the relationships between a and experimental measurements. These are summarized in Table V.1.

TABLE V.1

ACTIVITY RELATIONS

State of substance	Nature of activity
Gas	
Ideal	P (pressure, in atm.)
Real	f (fugacity) $= P\gamma$
Pure Solid	$a = 1$
Pure Liquid	$a = 1$
Solutions	
Nonelectrolytes	
Solvent	$a_1 = N_1\gamma_1$
Solute (practical standard state)	$a_2 = m\gamma_2$
Solute (unitary or rational	
standard state)	$a_2 = N_2\gamma_2$
Electrolytes	
Solvent	$a_1 = N_1\gamma_1$
Solute (e.g., NaCl)	$a_2 = m^2\gamma_2{}^2$

For a gas, a may usually be replaced by the pressure, or partial pressure in a mixture, P. For most biological problems, the gas pressure does not exceed one atmosphere, and for most gases, ideal behavior may be assumed at such low pressures. At higher pressures, it may be necessary to use a corrected pressure, $P\gamma$, where γ is the correction factor necessary to give correct answers in free energy calculations.

For a pure solid or a pure liquid, a is defined as 1. This is merely another way of saying that the pure solid or pure liquid is the standard state for that substance.

Our most common calculations will involve substances in solution. For the solvent, we always define the activity in terms of its mole-fraction N_1, and the correction fact γ_1, the activity coefficient; thus $a_1 = N_1\gamma_1$. In many solutions, the amount of dissolved solute, even if large in weight, does not contribute much to the total moles present and hence N_1 is frequently near unity. Likewise γ_1 is often near unity except in solutions containing high concentrations of solute.

When we turn to the solute we must distinguish between nonelectrolytes and electrolytes. In both types, the common or practical unit of concentration is the molality m. The activity of a nonelectrolyte a_2 is given by the product $m\gamma_2$. For an electrolyte, the result is more complicated, depending on the number of ions produced. For a uni-univalent electrolyte, e.g. NaCl, $a_2 = m^2\gamma_2^2$. For solutes in very dilute solution, γ_2 approaches unity, and hence a_2 can be replaced by m, or m^2, alone.

Finally, we should note that an alternative standard state, the unitary, or rational, standard state, has been used with some frequency recently in biochemical calculations. With this choice of standard state, we obtain "unitary free energies."[1] In essence this choice measures solute concentration in molefraction units, N_2, and a_2 becomes $N_2\gamma_2$.

Having defined the activity a in terms of experimental quantities, we should turn back briefly to a more precise specification of the meaning of $\Delta G°$, the standard free energy change. We shall now make the general and precise statement, that $\Delta G°$ is the free energy change for a reaction in which each of the participants is at an *activity of 1*. When it has an activity of unity, the substance is in its standard state. For an ideal gas, this means the gas at 1 atmosphere pressure. For a solute, this means when $a_2 = 1$. In the practical choice, the activity is unity somewhere near a molality of 1. If γ_2 is unimportant (i.e., essentially unity), then the activity is truly unity at unit molality, i.e., the standard state of the solute is the one-molal solution. In many problems the available data are not accurate enough to evaluate γ_2, and hence, to a first approximation we may set $a_2 = m$. If we choose the less common "unitary" standard state, then concentrations of solute are measured in molefraction, N_2, and the activity is unity when $N_2\gamma_2$ is unity.

[1] R. W. Gurney, *Ionic Processes in Solution*, McGraw-Hill, New York, 1953, page 90; W. Kauzmann, *Adv. Protein Chem.*, **14**, 1 (1959).

B. Illustrative Calculations

1. Free Energy of Dilution

Thus, in principle we can compute ΔG for any concentrations, if we know ΔG for any single set of specifications, at the same temperature. Such computations are essential in any transposition of free energy data from *in vitro* experiments to reasoning about behavior *in vivo*, for in physiological media concentrations of the participating substances may differ by orders of magnitude from those convenient for direct experimental measurement. Thus ΔG for a reaction occurring at physiological concentrations may be markedly different from $\Delta G°$, the change in free energy for standard conditions.

It is a simple matter to set up a general relationship between ΔG for any set of conditions and $\Delta G°$ which is normally provided in reference sources. We need merely add a suitable set of equations which express the necessary dilution steps and compute ΔG for each step by application of equation (5.1). For example, for the hydrolysis of adenosine triphosphate (ATP) to adenosine diphosphate (ADP) under standard conditions, which we may represent by,[2]

$$ATP^{4-} (1M) + H_2O \rightarrow ADP^{2-} (1M) + HPO_4^{2-} (1M);$$
$$\Delta G° = -7000 \text{ cal mole}^{-1} \quad (5.4)$$

the change in chemical potential is[3] near -7 kcal mole^{-1}. We should like to have ΔG for concentrations different from $1\ M$, e.g., physiological concentrations. To obtain this value let us add the following three equations to equation (5.4):

[2] For this problem, we will assume γ's are unity, and that concentrations of solute may be expressed in molarities.

[3] M. F. Morales, J. Botts, J. J. Blum, and T. L. Hill, *Physiol. Rev.*, **35**, 475 (1955).

ATP^{4-} (physiol conc) $\rightarrow ATP^{4-}$ $(1M)$;
$$\Delta G = RT \ln \left(1/C_{ATP(physiol\ conc)}\right) \quad (5.5)$$

ADP^{2-} $(1M) \rightarrow ADP^{2-}$ (physiol conc);
$$\Delta G = RT \ln \left(C_{ADP(physiol\ conc)}/1\right) \quad (5.6)$$

HPO_4^{2-} $(1M) \rightarrow HPO_4^{2-}$ (physiol conc);
$$\Delta G = RT \ln \left(C_{HPO_4(physiol\ conc)}/1\right) \quad (5.7)$$

The resultant of an addition of the chemical equations is

$$ATP^{4-} \text{ (physiol conc)} + H_2O \rightarrow ADP^{2-} \text{ (physiol conc)}$$
$$+ HPO_4^{2-} \text{ (physiol conc)} \quad (5.8)$$

which differs from (5.4) only in the concentrations of the participants. Since the chemical reaction (5.8) is obtained by addition of the chemical reactions in equations (5.4) to (5.7), ΔG for equation (5.8) is obtainable by summation of the ΔG's for (5.4) − (5.7). Hence we may write

$$
\begin{aligned}
\Delta G_{\substack{physiol \\ conditions}} &= \Delta G° + RT \ln \left(1/C_{ATP(physiol)}\right) \\
&\quad + RT \ln C_{ADP(physiol\ conc)} \\
&\quad + RT \ln C_{HPO_4(physiol\ conc)} \\
&= \Delta G° + RT \ln \left(C_{ADP}C_{HPO_4}/C_{ATP}\right)_{physiol\ conc}
\end{aligned} \quad (5.9)
$$

Numerical values for $\Delta G_{physiol}$ can be obtained only when the physiological concentrations of ATP, ADP, and HPO_4^{2-} can be estimated. Even without these concentrations, however, we can readily see that under physiological conditions ΔG is likely to be appreciably more negative than $\Delta G°$, which is −7 kcal mole^{-1}. As a rough guess one could assume that the concentrations of ATP and ADP would be of the same order of magnitude and thus would cancel inside the logarithm in (5.9). Hence the HPO_4^{2-} concentration, being a small decimal number, would make $RT \ln C_{HPO_4}$ a large negative number, to be added to −7 kcal mole^{-1} for $\Delta G°$. Thus ΔG for the hydrolysis of ATP at physiological concentrations would be appreciably more negative than 7 kcal mole^{-1}.

2. $\Delta G f°$ for Dissolved Substances

As a sample problem let us consider a calculation of the standard free energy of formation of succinic acid, HOOC—CH$_2$—CH$_2$—COOH, in aqueous solution at 25°, assuming that we know $\Delta G f°$ of solid succinic acid (see Table IV.2). To the equation, (5.10), for the formation of solid (CH$_2$COOH)$_2$ from its elements,

$$4C \text{ (graphite)} + 3H_2 \text{ (g)} + 2O_2 \text{ (g)} = \begin{matrix} CH_2COOH \\ | \\ CH_2COOH \end{matrix} \text{ (s)} \quad (5.10)$$

$$\Delta G f° = -178{,}680 \text{ cal mole}^{-1}$$

we add an equation for bringing the solid into a saturated aqueous solution,

$$\begin{matrix} CH_2COOH \\ | \\ CH_2COOH \end{matrix} \text{ (s)} = \begin{matrix} CH_2COOH \\ | \\ CH_2COOH \end{matrix} \text{ (aq, sat)}; \; \Delta G = 0 \quad (5.11)$$

For the reaction in (5.11) ΔG is zero since this is a transfer at equilibrium. Now we add further the equation

$$\begin{matrix} CH_2COOH \\ | \\ CH_2COOH \end{matrix} \text{ (aq, sat)} = \begin{matrix} CH_2COOH \\ | \\ CH_2COOH \end{matrix} \text{ (aq, } a_2 = 1); \; \Delta G = ? \quad (5.12)$$

For this transfer

$$\Delta G = RT \ln \frac{a_{\text{right}}}{a_{\text{left}}} \quad (5.13)$$

The activity on the right-hand side of equation (5.12) is unity by choice. For a_{left} we must keep in mind that we are dealing with *nonionized* succinic acid in the saturated aqueous solution at 25°. Hence:

$$a_{\text{left}} = m_{\substack{\text{nonionized} \\ \text{in sat soln}}} \; \gamma$$

$$= m_{\substack{\text{total} \\ \text{in sat soln}}} (1 - \text{fraction ionized})\gamma \quad (5.14)$$

The total concentration in the saturated solution, m_{total}, is easily measured experimentally. From the known pK_a of succinic acid in aqueous solution, or an appropriate pH measurement, one can compute the fraction ionized. The activity coefficient must be obtained from suitable measurements of the colligative properties of this solution. All of this information has been accumulated experimentally. Hence we may write:

$$a_{\text{left}} = (0.715)(1 - 0.0112)(0.87) \qquad (5.15)$$

Inserting this information into equation (5.13) we find:

$$\Delta G = 290 \text{ cal mole}^{-1} \qquad (5.16)$$

and this is the quantity to be used for the free energy change of reaction (5.12). Thus if we add equations (5.10)–(5.12) we obtain:

$$4C \text{ (graphite)} + 3H_2 \text{ (g)} + 2O_2 \text{ (g)} = \begin{array}{c} CH_2COOH \\ | \\ CH_2COOH \end{array} \text{(aq)} \qquad (5.17)$$

$$\Delta Gf^{\circ} = -178{,}390 \text{ cal mole}^{-1}$$

This is the way in which the value listed in Table IV.2 was obtained.

We can extend this problem by now asking for ΔGf° of monosuccinate ion, $(CH_2COOH)(CH_2COO^-)$, in solution. This free energy of formation is obtained by adding the following equation to (5.17):

$$\begin{array}{c} CH_2COOH \\ | \\ CH_2COOH \end{array} \text{(aq, } a_2 = 1) = H^+ \text{ (aq, } a_2 = 1) + \begin{array}{c} CH_2—COO^- \\ | \\ CH_2COOH \end{array} \text{(aq, } a_2 = 1)$$

$$\Delta G^{\circ} = ? \quad (5.18)$$

Since every participant in this reaction is in its standard state, one procedure for calculating the corresponding ΔG° merely makes use of the equation [see equation (4.1)],

$$\Delta G^{\circ} = -RT \ln K = +1365 \, pK_{a_1} = 5700 \text{ cal mole}^{-1} \quad (5.19)$$

where K_{a_1} is the first acidity constant of succinic acid,

$10^{-4.184}$. Addition of equations (5.17) and (5.18) then gives

$$4C + 3H_2 + 2O_2 = H^+ \text{ (aq)} + \begin{matrix} CH_2COO^- \\ | \\ CH_2COOH \end{matrix} \text{ (aq)}$$
$$\Delta Gf^\circ = -172,690 \text{ cal mole}^{-1} \qquad (5.20)$$

This is as far as one can proceed experimentally. For concise representation in tables, however, we agree to the following convention:

$$H^+ \text{ (aq, } a_2 = 1) = \tfrac{1}{2}H_2 \text{ (g, } a = 1); \ \Delta G^\circ = -\Delta Gf^\circ \equiv 0 \ (5.21)$$

In essence we arbitrarily define the standard free energy of formation of the H^+ ion as zero, in analogy to the corresponding convention with regard to $\mathscr{E}^\circ$ for the H_2/H^+ electrode. Thus, if we add equation (5.21) to (5.20) we obtain ΔGf° of monosuccinate ion:

$$4C + 2\tfrac{1}{2}H_2 + 2O_2 = \begin{matrix} CH_2COO^- \\ | \\ CH_2COOH \end{matrix} \text{ (aq)}; \qquad (5.22)$$
$$\Delta Gf^\circ = -172,690 \text{ cal mole}^{-1}$$

We must recognize, however, that the actual ΔGf° of a single ion in solution has not been (and in fact cannot be) determined. Values listed in Table IV.2 for ions are all relative values, relative to a conventional reference point of zero for H^+ ion.

Proceeding further with succinic acid we could obtain ΔGf° for the di-anion by adding the equation:

$$\begin{matrix} CH_2COO^- \\ | \\ CH_2COOH \end{matrix} \text{ (aq, } a_2 = 1) = H^+ \text{ (aq, } a_2 = 1) + \begin{matrix} CH_2COO^- \\ | \\ CH_2COO^- \end{matrix} \text{ (aq, } a_2 = 1)$$
$$\Delta G^\circ = 1365 \text{ p}K_{a_2} \qquad (5.23)$$

to equation (5.20). Thereby we obtain:

$$4C + 3H_2 + 2O_2 = 2H^+ \text{ (aq)} + (CH_2COO^-)_2 \text{ (aq)}$$
$$\Delta Gf^\circ = -164,970 \text{ cal mole}^{-1} \qquad (5.24)$$

Again, if we recognize the convention of equation (5.21),

the $\Delta Gf°$ of succinate^{2-} is automatically $-164,970$ cal mole^{-1} (see Table IV.2).

Finally, in connection with the succinate problem, we should turn to one further consideration. Biochemical reactions are of primary interest at physiological pH. It is convenient, therefore, to know thermodynamic quantities at pH 7. To find the free energy of formation of succinate^{2-}, for example, at pH 7, we add to equation (5.24) the following equation:

$$2H^+ \, (aq, \, a_2 = 1) = 2H^+ \, (a_2 = 10^{-7});$$
$$\Delta G = 2RT \ln (10^{-7}/1) = -19,100 \text{ cal} \quad (5.25)$$

Thus we obtain:

$$4C + 3H_2 + 2O_2 = 2H^+ \, (a_2 = 10^{-7})$$
$$+ (CH_2COO^-)_2 \, (aq, \, a_2 = 1)$$
$$\Delta Gf \equiv \Delta Gf°' = -184,070 \text{ cal mole}^{-1} \quad (5.26)$$

Since every participant in reaction (5.26) except the H^+ ion is in its standard state, we agree to call the ΔGf a $\Delta Gf°'$, the prime emphasizing that the H^+ is not at unit activity. Here too we can agree further that:

$$\tfrac{1}{2}H_2 = H^+ \, (a_2 = 10^{-7}); \, \Delta Gf°' = 0 \quad (5.27)$$

In this case then $\Delta Gf°'$ of succinate^{-2} ion at pH 7 is automatically -184.07 kcal mole^{-1}.

Let us consider another example of a $\Delta G°$ calculation for a dissolved substance, one in which a gas is involved. For the first step in the oxygenation of hemoglobin at 19°,

$$Hb \, (aq) + O_2 \, (g) = HbO_2 \, (aq);$$
$$\Delta G° = -2590 \text{ cal mole}^{-1} \quad (5.28)$$

The $\Delta G°$ was computed from the known value of 85.5 atm^{-1} for the equilibrium constant for this reaction at 19°. Let us now try to find $\Delta G°$ for the corresponding reaction with O_2 (aq, $a_2 = 1$) instead of O_2 (g).

For this calculation we shall make use of the known

solubilities of our oxygen in water. At 19°, in equilibrium with air (in which the partial pressure of oxygen is 0.2 atm) the solubility of oxygen in water is 0.00023 molal.

Let us consider, therefore, the following three transfers of oxygen, for each of which we can readily calculate ΔG:

$$O_2 \ (g, P = 1) = O_2 \ (g, P = 0.2);$$
$$\Delta G = RT \ln (0.2/1) = -940 \text{ cal mole}^{-1} \quad (5.29)$$

$$O_2 \ (g, P = 0.2) = O_2 \ (aq, sat); \ \Delta G = 0 \text{ (equil)} \quad (5.30)$$

$$O_2 \ (aq, sat) = O_2 \ (aq, a_2 = 1);$$
$$\Delta G = RT \ln (1/0.00023) = 4870 \text{ cal mole}^{-1} \quad (5.31)$$

The net result of the addition of these three equations is:

$$O_2 \ (g) = O_2 \ (aq); \ \Delta G° = 3930 \text{ cal mole}^{-1} \quad (5.32)$$

Subtracting this equation from (5.28) gives us:

$$Hb \ (aq) + O_2 \ (aq) = HbO_2 \ (aq);$$
$$\Delta G° = -6520 \text{ cal mole}^{-1} \quad (5.33)$$

3. Free Energy of Hydrophobic Bonds

In essence, the stability of the hydrophobic bond is attributed to the tendency of an apolar group to remain in an apolar environment rather than to go out into a surrounding aqueous environment. Thus, one method of evaluating the stability of this bond is to determine the free energy of transfer, $\Delta Gt°$, of an apolar group from an organic environment to water. A number of such calculations have been made and lead to positive values of $\Delta Gt°$ for apolar groups.

Since hydrophobic bonds are of special interest in protein molecules, it would be particularly desirable to evaluate $\Delta Gt°$ for apolar amino-acid side chains. However, these side chains cannot be plucked off by themselves. Nevertheless, a reasonable assumption is that:

$$\Delta Gt^\circ \ [\text{R—CH(NH}_3{}^+)\text{COO}^-] - \Delta Gt^\circ \ [\text{CH}_2(\text{NH}_3{}^+)\text{COO}^-]$$
$$= \Delta Gt^\circ \ (\text{R group}) \quad (5.34)$$

that is, that the free energy of transfer of the amino acid R—CH(NH$_3{}^+$)COO$^-$ is composed of two parts, that of the apolar R group, and that of the zwitterion base which may be approximated by glycine, CH$_2$(NH$_3{}^+$)COO$^-$.

Since amino acids and particularly glycine are not very soluble in very nonpolar solvents, such as benzene or hexane, we must settle for alcohol as the prototype nonpolar solvent. Thus we have reduced our problem to the measurement of ΔGt° of various amino acids as they are transferred from alcohol to water. Since the procedure is the same for all the amino acids, we shall consider a detailed calculation for only one, glycine.

The transfer process cannot be conveniently carried out directly, at least not for thermodynamic computations. A series of steps that can make use of the most readily accessible experimental data are the following:

$$\text{Gly (alcohol, sat soln)} = \text{Gly (s)}; \ \Delta G = 0 \quad (5.35)$$

$$\text{Gly (alcohol, } a_2 = 1) = \text{Gly (alcohol, sat soln)}$$
$$\Delta G = RT \ln \frac{N_{\text{alc}}^{\text{sat}} \ \gamma_{\text{alc}}^{\text{sat}}}{1} \quad (5.36)$$

$$\text{Gly (s)} = \text{Gly (aq, sat soln)}; \ \Delta G = 0 \quad (5.37)$$

$$\text{Gly (aq, sat soln)} = \text{Gly (aq, } a_2 = 1);$$
$$\Delta G = RT \ln \frac{1}{N_{\text{aq}}^{\text{sat}} \ \gamma_{\text{aq}}^{\text{sat}}} \quad (5.38)$$

For (5.35) and (5.37) ΔG is zero since each of these is an equilibrium process. For the transfer in equation (5.36), ΔG is calculated by applying equation (5.3) using the unitary (or rational) standard state in which a of the solute is replaced by its molefraction. The same procedure is used in (5.38). Thus, what we need to find are the solubilities of glycine in alcohol and in water, respectively, N_{alc}^{sat} and N_{aq}^{sat}, and the corresponding activity coefficients. These data have been accumulated[4] from the literature.

If we now add equations (5.35)–(5.38), we obtain

$$\text{Gly (alc, } a_2 = 1) = \text{Gly (aq, } a_2 = 1)$$

$$\Delta G = \Delta Gt^{\circ} = RT \ln \frac{N_{alc}^{sat}}{N_{aq}^{sat}} + RT \ln \frac{\gamma_{alc}^{sat}}{\gamma_{aq}^{sat}} \qquad (5.39)$$

In actual computations, the γ's must often be approximated. However, their contribution to ΔGt° is always small compared to that of the N_{sat}'s.

From the solubilities alone, the values listed in Table V.2 have been calculated for glycine and for a series of

TABLE V.2
UNITARY FREE ENERGIES OF TRANSFER
FROM ALCOHOL TO WATER AT 25°

Amino Acid	ΔGt°	ΔG° (R group)
Gly	−4630	(0)
Ala	−3900	730
Val	−2940	1690
Leu	−2210	2420
Ile	−1690	2970
Phe	−1980	2650
Pro	−2060	2600

amino acids with apolar side chains. For all of these, the free energy of transfer from alcohol to water is negative; that is, the transfer to an aqueous environment would occur spontaneously. However this ΔGt° is composed of a contribution from the highly charged dipolar ion, $CH(NH_3^+)COO^-$, as well as from the apolar R. If in each case we take the difference ΔG° as directed by equa-

[4]C. Tanford, *J. Am. Chem. Soc.*, **84**, 4240 (1962); Y. Nozaki and C. Tanford, *J. Biol. Chem.*, **238**, 4074 (1963).

tion (5.34) we obtain the values listed in the last column of Table V.2. Here we have a measure of the stability of the hydrophobic side chain, R. For isoleucine, Ile, for example, an input of 2970 cal mole^{-1} of free energy would be necessary to move the R group from the apolar environment to water. Correspondingly large free energies are necessary to move the other bulky apolar side chains. These numbers provide one basis for attempts to account for protein stability in terms of hydrophobic bonding.

Exercises

I. The hydrolysis of hippuric acid,

Benzoylglycine + H$_2$O → benzoic acid + glycine (1)

may be examined thermodynamically under a variety of conditions. Data necessary for some thermodynamic computations may be obtained from Table IV in the article by F. H. Carpenter, *J. Am. Chem. Soc.*, **82**, 1111 (1960).

(A) Consider first the situation in which all the components in (1) (at 298°K) except water are in the solid state, H$_2$O being liquid.

 (a) Using data for $\Delta Hf°$ find $\Delta H°$ for reaction (1).
 (b) Using $S°$ data find $\Delta S°$ for reaction (1).
 (c) Compute $\Delta G°$ for hydrolysis under these conditions.

(B) To compute $\Delta G°$ (at 298°K) for reaction (1) with all substances dissolved in aqueous solution, we must find ΔG for transferring each substance from the solid state to solution.

 (a) The solubility of benzoic acid in water is 0.028 molal. Its pK_a is 4.20. The activity coefficient, γ, of the nonionized form in saturated aqueous solution is 1. Find $\Delta Gf°$ of nonionized benzoic acid in aqueous solution.

(b) Find $\Delta Gf°$ of H^+ + benzoate ion in aqueous solution.

(c) Starting with the $\Delta Gf°$ of (dissolved) non-ionized hippuric acid, find $\Delta Gf°$ of H^+ + hippurate ion in aqueous solution.

(d) Compute $\Delta G°$ for reaction (1) with each component in solution at pH 6–7 (i.e., glycine isoelectric, hippuric and benzoic acids as the anions).

II. The equilibrium constants for the oxygenation reaction

$$O_2 \text{ (g)} + \text{Hr (aq)} = \text{HrO}_2 \text{ (aq)} \tag{2}$$

where Hr represents hemerythrin (the oxygen-carrying pigment of *Golfingia gouldii*) are:

t°C	K (atm^{-1})
0	9120
25	380

(A) Using the thermodynamic relation

$$\frac{d \ln K}{dT} = \frac{\Delta H°}{RT^2}$$

find $\Delta H°$, the heat of oxygenation.

(B) Find $\Delta S°$, the entropy change for reaction (2) at 25°C.

(C) Find $\Delta G°$ for the reaction:

$$O_2 \text{ (aq)} + \text{Hr (aq)} = \text{HrO}_2 \text{ (aq)} \tag{3}$$

III. The standard free energy of formation of L-alanine (s) is listed in Table IV.2. The solubility of L-Ala in water at 25°C is 1.87 molal, and its activity coefficient in a saturated solution is 1.05. Its acidity constants are: $pK_1 = 2.34$; $pK_2 = 9.69$.

(A) Find $\Delta Gf°$ for L-Ala (aq). Compare your answer with that in Table IV.2.

(B) Find $\Delta Gf°$ of L-Ala^{1-}.

(C) Find $\Delta Gf°$ of L-Ala^{1+}. (*Answer*: -99.19 kcal mole^{-1}.)

IV. The solubility[5] of phenylalanine in water at 25° is 0.170 moles/kg solvent, and in aqueous 6-molar urea is 0.263 moles/kg solvent. Find the standard free energy of transfer of phenylalanine from water to aqueous urea solution using molalities as the concentration units and neglecting γ's.

Answer: -260 cal mole^{-1}.

The corresponding $\Delta Gt°$ for glycine is near zero. Does urea strengthen or weaken hydrophobic bonds?

[5] See footnote on p. 48.

VI. GROUP TRANSFER POTENTIAL: "HIGH-ENERGY BOND"

One of the most useful concepts in quantitative biology, particularly in correlating the biochemical changes in intermediary metabolism, is that of the "high-energy bond." There are certain valid objections to the name, however, especially that it gives a misleading impression as to the nature of the quantity being considered. Since fundamentally, as we shall see shortly, we are talking about changes in chemical potential, ΔG, when certain groups are transferred from one molecule to another, a more appropriate name might be *group-transfer potential*.

A. Comparison of Transfer Potentials

There are in fact a number of other *transfer potentials* that are used in biochemical energetics, for example, *acidity* measured in terms of pK_a, and *oxidation-reduction potentials* measured in terms of $\mathscr{E}^0$. All of these transfer potentials are modified, or derivative, forms of the free energy. It may be illuminating, therefore, to compare certain common features of these three types of transfer potential (Table VI.1).

In all cases the potential refers to some chemical transformation, usually written in a very concise form. For example, we generally write the reaction.

$$AH \rightarrow A^- + H^+ \tag{6.1}$$

in discussions of acidity. However, it is necessary to realize that this equation is only a short-hand notation. If taken literally as meaning the removal of a proton from the acid AH, then reaction (6.1), for all practical purposes would never occur; for example, to remove a proton from NH_4^+ to give NH_3 requires an *input* of energy of some 300,000 cal mole^{-1} (in the gas phase). The actual meaning of equation (6.1) to chemists is not its literal one, however. Rather it is recognized that the proton is actually *transferred* from AH to some acceptor species, for example water:

$$AH + H_2O = A^- + H_3O^+ \qquad (6.2)$$

For this transfer reaction the energy change is usually of the order of a few kilocalories, positive or negative, and the transfer does occur to a greater or lesser extent depending on the magnitude of ΔG.

TABLE VI.1
COMPARISON OF TYPES OF TRANSFER POTENTIAL

	Proton-transfer potential (acidity)	Electron-transfer potential (redox potential)	Group-transfer potential (high-energy bond)
Concise equation	$AH \to A^- + H^+$	$A \to A^+ + e$	$A \sim PO_4 \to$ $A + PO_4$
Equation with acceptor	$AH + H_2O \to$ $A^- + H_3O^+$	$A + H^+ \to$ $A^+ + \frac{1}{2}H_2$	$A \sim PO_4 + H_2O \to$ $A{-}OH + HPO_4$
Measure of transfer potential	$pK_a = \dfrac{\Delta G^\circ}{2.303\, RT}$	$\mathscr{E}^\circ = -\dfrac{\Delta G^\circ}{n\mathscr{F}}$	$\Delta Gh^\circ = \Delta G^\circ$
Nature of transfer potential	$\propto \Delta G^\circ$ per mole H^+ transferred	$\propto \Delta G^\circ$ per mole e transferred	$\propto \Delta G^\circ$ per mole PO_4 transferred

Similarly for electron transfer potentials, *redox potentials*, we usually write the concise equation

$$A \to A^+ + e \qquad (6.3)$$

or, in the now almost universal convention, in the
reverse direction. Again, as written, equation (6.3)
implies that it is describing the ionization process and
this would rarely happen in circumstances of biochemical interest, for the *input* of energy required to remove
an electron from, for example, an Fe^{2+} atom to give
Fe^{3+} is of the order of 10^5 cal. In discussions of redox
potentials, however, the student at an early stage is
made aware that implicit in equation (6.3) is the presence
of an acceptor, and that the actual reaction is described
better by the equation

$$A + H^+ = A^+ + \tfrac{1}{2}H_2 \tag{6.4}$$

For this electron transfer process, the energy change is
again of the order of a few kilocalories, positive or negative, and the reaction does occur to a greater or lesser
extent depending on the magnitude of ΔG.

Likewise, in connection with biochemical *bond
energies* we must make a corresponding distinction
between the concise representation and the more
detailed description of the process implied. The term
"bond energy" has a very definite meaning in the field
of energetics, quite different from that implied by the
biochemical term "high-energy bond." The outstanding
example of a compound with a high phosphate-transfer
potential is adenosine triphosphate, in which the
"high-energy bond" is symbolized by $\sim$:

$$Ad—Rib—P \sim P \sim P$$

The implication of the name "high-energy bond" is
that there is a concentration of energy between $P \sim P$
which tends to make the terminal phosphate fly off
whenever possible. The $P \sim P$ bond will not spontaneously spring open, however. Actually, one would have
to put energy *into* ATP, approximately 10^5 cal mole^{-1},
to remove the terminal phosphate group, or, more
explicitly, to break the distal P—O—P bonding:

$$
\begin{array}{c}
\quad\;\; \overset{O}{\overset{\|}{}} \quad\;\; \overset{O}{\overset{\|}{}} \quad\;\; \overset{O}{\overset{\|}{}} \\
Ad\!-\!Rib\!-\!O\!-\!P\!-\!O\!-\!P\!-\!O\!-\!P\!-\!O^- \\
\quad\;\; \underset{O^-}{|} \quad\;\; \underset{O^-}{|} \quad\;\; \underset{O^-}{|}
\end{array}
$$

This energy which must be forced into the molecule to break a bond between two atoms[1] is what should be called the bond energy (Fig. VI.1).

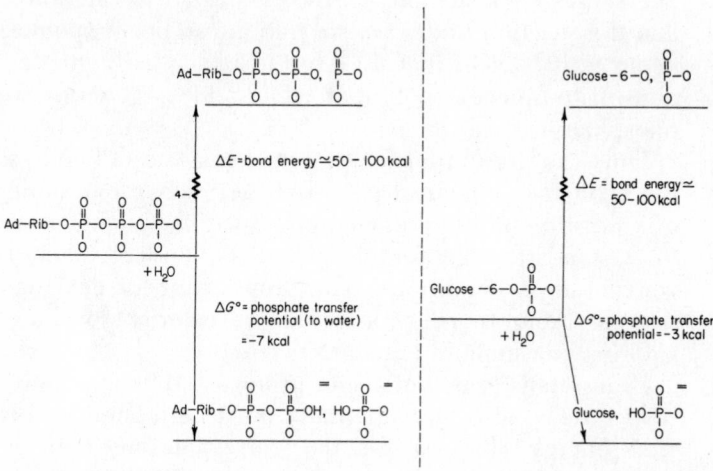

FIG. VI.1. Distinction between bond energy and group transfer potential.

On the other hand, the biochemist is not really interested in the change in internal energy necessary to break the P—O bond, but rather in the change in chemical potential (or free energy) when a compound such as, for example, ATP transfers one of its substituent groups to another molecule. ΔG for such a transfer reaction obviously ought to depend on the nature of the acceptor molecule as well as on the character of the group donor. Since we are primarily interested in *comparing* group-transfer potentials of a variety of donor molecules, it

[1] Strictly speaking, this reaction should be carried out in the gaseous state if we wish to call ΔE the bond energy.

becomes convenient to select some standard acceptor molecule. This is usually H_2O. Thus, as is shown in Fig. VI.1, the change in chemical potential when the terminal phosphate group is transferred from ATP^{4-} to H_2O, with the concomitant formation of ADP^{2-} and HPO_4^{2-}, is -7 kcal $mole^{-1}$. On the other hand, when glucose 6-phosphate^{2-} transfers its phosphate group to water, $\Delta G°$ is only -3 kcal $mole^{-1}$. Since a negative ΔG signifies that the reaction under consideration can occur spontaneously, it is clear that ATP has a substantially greater phosphate-transfer potential than does glucose 6-phosphate.

Thus the group-transfer potential may be defined as the change in chemical potential, $\Delta G°$, when one mole of a substituent group of a donor molecule is transferred to a standard acceptor, usually H_2O, under standard concentration conditions. The proper unit for designation of group-transfer potentials is calories (or kilocalories) per mole of transferred group.

Group-transfer potentials for protons and for electrons, respectively, also fundamentally must be related to the free energy changes for the corresponding transfer processes. However, historically, other quantities which served as quantitative measures of the extent of transfer came into general use before their relation to free energy was widely appreciated. Nevertheless, these quantities, pK_a for acidity, and $\mathscr{E}°$ for redox potentials, must be proportional to $\Delta G°$. Thus, it follows from equation (4.1) that

$$pK_a = \frac{\Delta G°}{2.303RT} \qquad (6.5)$$

where pK_a refers to the reaction represented concisely by equation (6.1). Since a high pK_a implies a large (positive) $\Delta G°$, the dissociation of a proton would not be favored, and the acid would be weak. Contrariwise, a lower pK_a implies a stronger acid. The pK_a transfer potential is thus proportional to $\Delta G°$ for the transfer of a mole of protons from the acid to a reference acceptor molecule [equation (6.2)].

Similarly $\mathscr{E}°$ is proportional to $\Delta G°$. Thus it follows from equation (4.7) that

$$\mathscr{E}° = -\frac{\Delta G°}{n\mathscr{F}} \qquad (6.6)$$

By general convention among biochemists and most physical chemists, $\mathscr{E}°$ is agreed upon to refer to the reverse of equation (6.3); in other words, tables of $\mathscr{E}°$ values apply to the process

$$e + A^+ \rightarrow A \qquad (6.7)$$

Thus if $\mathscr{E}°$ is a positive number, $\Delta G°$ is negative and the uptake of an electron by A^+ occurs spontaneously. Furthermore the more positive is $\mathscr{E}°$, the stronger oxidizing agent is A^+. Thus the $\mathscr{E}°$ transfer potential is proportional to $\Delta G°$ for the transfer of a mole of electrons from an acceptor to the substance of interest:

$$\tfrac{1}{2}H_2 + A^+ \rightarrow H^+ + A \qquad (6.8)$$

B. Coupled Reactions

The primary biological usefulness of $\mathscr{E}°$'s is for decisions as to whether certain oxidation-reduction reactions are feasible, within the principles of energetics. Likewise, the main use of group-transfer potentials is to decide whether particular transfer reactions are compatible with thermodynamic requirements. For example, in the conversion of arginine to arginine phosphate,

$$\underset{\underset{\text{H}_2\text{N—C—NH—(CH}_2)_3\text{—CH—COO}^-}{\overset{\overset{\text{NH}_2^+}{\|}}{}\overset{\overset{\text{NH}_3^+}{|}}{}}}{} + \text{HPO}_4^{2-} \rightarrow$$

$$\underset{\underset{{}^=\text{O}_3\text{P—NH—C—NH—(CH}_2)_3\text{—CH—COO}^-}{\overset{\overset{\text{NH}_2^+}{\|}}{}\overset{\overset{\text{NH}_3^+}{|}}{}}}{} + \text{H}_2\text{O}$$

$$\Delta G° = +7 \text{ kcal mole}^{-1} \qquad (6.9)$$

the chemical potential must be increased by 7 kcal mole^{-1}. Clearly, then, this reaction cannot occur by itself (at standard, $1M$, concentrations). If, however, another reaction can take place concurrently with a $\Delta G°$ of -7 kcal mole^{-1} or more negative, then the net reaction would be thermodynamically feasible. For example, we can combine the following two reactions

$$\text{ATP} + \text{H}_2\text{O} \rightarrow \text{ADP} + \text{HPO}_4{}^{2-}; \qquad \Delta G° = -7 \text{ kcal mole}^{-1} \quad (6.10)$$

$$\text{Arginine} + \text{HPO}_4{}^{2-} \rightarrow \text{Arginine-P} + \text{H}_2\text{O};$$
$$\Delta G° = +7 \text{ kcal mole}^{-1} \quad (6.11)$$

to obtain by addition

$$\text{ATP} + \text{Arginine} = \text{ADP} + \text{Arginine-P}; \qquad \Delta G° = 0 \quad (6.12)$$

The resultant reaction will occur to an appreciable extent since, if the standard ΔG is zero, the equilibrium concentrations of ADP and arginine phosphate will be 1 molar in the presence of 1 molar ATP and one-molar arginine.

On the other hand, addition of the following two reactions

$$\text{Glucose 6-P} + \text{H}_2\text{O} \rightarrow \text{glucose} + \text{HPO}_4{}^{2-};$$
$$\Delta G° = -3 \text{ kcal mole}^{-1} \quad (6.13)$$
$$\text{Arginine} + \text{HPO}_4{}^{2-} \rightarrow \text{Arginine-P} + \text{H}_2\text{O};$$
$$\Delta G° = +7 \text{ kcal mole}^{-1} \quad (6.11)$$

leads to

$$\text{Glucose 6-P} + \text{Arginine} \rightarrow \text{Glucose} + \text{Arginine-P};$$
$$\Delta G° = +4 \text{ kcal mole}^{-1} \quad (6.14)$$

for which the net change in chemical potential is a substantial positive number. Thus, reaction (6.14) cannot occur (under standard conditions).

Consequently we might say, speaking rather loosely, that when reaction (6.10) is "coupled" with (6.11), the phosphorylation of arginine is made to proceed, but when reaction (6.13) is "coupled" with (6.11), the phosphorylation of arginine nonetheless cannot be produced. Alternatively (Fig. VI.2) we might recognize that the phosphate-transfer potential of ATP is high and

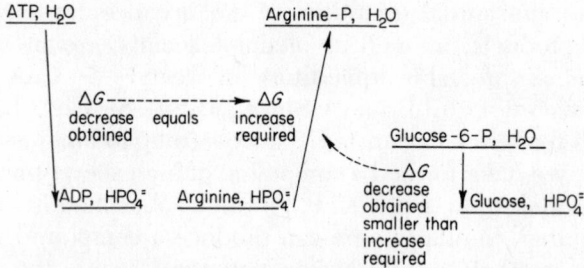

FIG. VI.2. Coupling of potentials, or "energy coupling."

hence adequate to place a phosphate group on arginine despite the counter-potential of almost the same magnitude of arginine phosphate.[2] On the other hand, the phosphate-transfer potential of glucose-6-phosphate is only -3 kcal mole^{-1}, which is inadequate to place a phosphate group on arginine since the back-potential of arginine phosphate is greater, -7 kcal mole^{-1}.

Coupling of potentials is not limited to reactions involving transfer of the same group in both cases. For example, the free energy liberated when a pyrophosphate group is transferred from ATP to water, with the concomitant formation of adenosine monophosphate (AMP) and pyrophosphate (PP), may be used to supply the free energy required to form an acetyl-thiol ester of high transfer potential. The individual reactions,

$$ATP + H_2O \rightarrow AMP + PP; \quad \Delta G° = -7 \text{ kcal mole}^{-1} \quad (6.15)$$

$$CH_3COOH + HS{-}CoA^3 \rightarrow CH_3COS{-}CoA + H_2O;$$
$$\Delta G° \simeq +7 \text{ kcal mole}^{-1} (6.16)$$

if coupled, lead to

$$ATP + CH_3COOH + HS{-}CoA = AMP + PP$$
$$+ CH_3COS{-}CoA; \quad \Delta G° \simeq 0 \ (6.17)$$

The value of $\Delta G°$ indicates that equilibrium is attained

[2] The phosphate-transfer potential of arginine phosphate is -7 kcal mole^{-1}, as can be seen by changing reaction (6.11) to read from right to left.

[3] HS—CoA represents Coenzyme A.

when substantial quantities (1 molar concentrations) of the products, as well as of the reactants, are present. Thus, appreciable quantities of acetyl—S—CoA are formed at equilibrium.[4] Since acetyl—S—CoA has a high tendency to transfer its acetyl group to other acceptors, we have formed a compound of high acetyl-transfer potential from one, ATP, of high phosphate-transfer potential. Similarly, one can produce a compound with high methyl-group transfer potential[5] using the free energy obtainable from the hydrolytic splitting of the phosphate groups of high transfer potential in ATP.

Considerations of relative group-transfer potentials (Fig. VI.3) tell us whether a particular combination of reactions is thermodynamically feasible. An affirmative answer does not mean, however, that the molecular coupling, or the actual molecular mechanism of the transformation, is the same as the reactions whose potentials have been coupled. The resultant ΔG of a reaction depends only on the initial and final reactants, and on their states, but not on the actual molecular mechanism through which the reaction occurs. Thus, for reaction (6.17) $\Delta G°$ is zero whether the reaction occurs through steps (6.15) and (6.16) or (as is known to be the case) through a more complicated sequence of steps. Classical energetics, since it is independent of the assumptions of atomic theory, can give no information on mechanisms at the molecular level.

C. Experimental Determination of Group Transfer Potentials

We shall examine in some detail the experimental data that must be accumulated to evaluate the power of a particular high-energy bond. In the course of these computations we shall also specify the nature of the reactions more precisely.

[4] J. R. Stern, B. Shapiro, E. R. Stadtman, and S. Ochoa, *J. Biol. Chem.*, **193**, 703 (1951); M. E. Jones, *Federation Proc.*, **12**, 708 (1953).

[5] G. L. Cantoni, *J. Biol. Chem.*, **204**, 403 (1953).

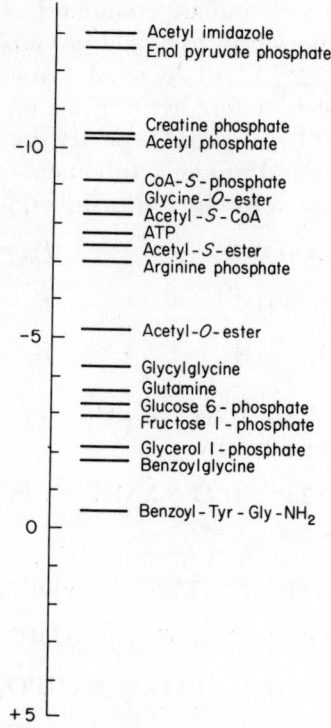

FIG. VI.3. Group transfer potentials (kcal mole⁻¹), pH 7, 25°C.

1. Phosphate Bond Energy

For precise calculations we must recognize at the outset that at physiological pH, ionizing molecules frequently exist in more than one (charged) form. Thus in ATP for example, three of the phosphate hydroxyl groups have pK_a's near 1–2, and are completely ionized at pH's around 7, but the fourth hydroxyl has a pK_a of 6.50 and hence is only partially dissociated at most pH's of biochemical interest. Before writing an equation for the hydrolysis of ATP, we should specify the charged forms of each reactant and product. In concise notation these may be represented by the following equilibria:

$$ATP^{3-} = ATP^{4-} + H^+ \qquad\qquad K_\alpha = 10^{-6.50} \quad (6.18)$$

$$ADP^{2-} = ADP^{3-} + H^+ \qquad\qquad K_\beta = 10^{-6.27} \quad (6.19)$$

$$H_2PO_4^- = HPO_4^{2-} + H^+ \qquad\qquad K_\gamma = 10^{-6.73} \quad (6.20)$$

Thus the hydrolysis of ATP at pH 7, for example, really should be represented by

$$\Sigma ATP + H_2O = \Sigma ADP + \Sigma PO_4 \qquad (6.21)$$

where

$$[\Sigma ATP] = [ATP^{3-}] + [ATP^{4-}] \qquad (6.22)$$

$$[\Sigma ADP] = [ADP^{2-}] + [ADP^{3-}] \qquad (6.23)$$

$$[\Sigma PO_4] = [H_2PO_4^-] + [HPO_4^{2-}] \qquad (6.24)$$

The standard free energy change, $\Delta G°$, for reaction (6.21) refers, therefore, to ΔG for *total* concentration of ATP, ΣATP, at unit activity, and for the *total* concentrations of ADP and PO_4, respectively, at unit activity.

To actually evaluate this $\Delta G°$ we turn to experimental measurements of equilibrium constants. The equilibrium constant for equation (6.21) lies so far to the right, that is, the hydrolysis of ATP is so nearly complete at equilibrium, that K_Σ

$$K_\Sigma = \frac{[\Sigma ADP]\,[\Sigma PO_4]}{[\Sigma ATP]} \qquad (6.25)$$

cannot be evaluated directly. However, we can couple

this reaction with another, the synthesis of glutamine, Gln, from glutamic acid, Glu^-, and ammonium ion,

$$Glu^- + NH_4^+ = Gln + H_2O \qquad (6.26)$$

for which the equilibrium constant, K_G, is known:

$$K_G = \frac{[Gln]}{[Glu^-][NH_4^+]} = 0.00315 \text{ (at pH 7, 310°K)} \quad (6.27)$$

The coupled reaction

$$Glu^- + NH_4^+ + \Sigma ATP = Gln + \Sigma ADP + \Sigma PO_4 \quad (6.28)$$

will attain equilibrium in the presence of an enzyme glutamine synthetase, and the equilibrium constant, K', has been measured:

$$K' = \frac{[Gln][\Sigma ADP][\Sigma PO_4]}{[Glu^-][NH_4^+][\Sigma ATP]}$$
$$= 1200 \text{ (at pH 7, 310°K)} \quad (6.29)$$

Inspection of equations (6.25), (6.27) and (6.29) shows that

$$K' = K_\Sigma K_G \qquad (6.30)$$

Therefore,

$$K_\Sigma = 3.8 \times 10^5 \qquad (6.31)$$

and

$$\Delta G^{\circ\prime} = -RT \ln K_\Sigma = -7900 \text{ cal mole}^{-1} \qquad (6.32)$$

at 310°K. Thus the phosphate bond energy, or transfer potential, in ATP at pH 7 (and 37°C) is -7.9 kcal mole^{-1}.

2. *Variation of Transfer Potential with Standard Species Chosen*

In the preceding section we have considered the bond energy of ATP under "practical" conditions, that is, in a solution in which various ionic species exist. For some purposes we might wish to know the intrinsic transfer potential of a single charged species going to products in only one ionic state each. For example, we might consider the reaction

$$ATP^{4-} + H_2O = ADP^{2-} + HPO_4^{2-} \qquad (6.33)$$

$\Delta G°$ for this reaction refers to ΔG for ATP^{4-} being at a concentration corresponding to unit activity *regardless* of what the concentration of ATP^{3-} or ΣATP might be. Similarly it refers to concentrations of unit activity for ADP^{2-} and HPO_4^{2-}, respectively. Thus $\Delta G°$ for equation (6.33) need not be the same as $\Delta G°'$ for equation (6.21). Nevertheless these two standard ΔG's are related to each other, because the corresponding equilibrium constants are interdependent.

Thus for equation (6.33), we may write an equilibrium constant

$$K = \frac{[ADP^{2-}]\,[HPO_4^{2-}]}{[ATP^{4-}]} \qquad (6.34)$$

But each concentration factor in (6.34) may be related to a corresponding concentration sum $[\Sigma]$. For example, from equation (6.22) we have

$$[ATP^{4-}] = [\Sigma ATP] - [ATP^{3-}] \qquad (6.35)$$

If we also make use of the information in equation (6.18), we obtain

$$[ATP^{3-}] = \frac{[H^+]\,[ATP^{4-}]}{K_\alpha} \qquad (6.36)$$

which can be inserted into (6.35) and the resultant rearranged to give

$$[ATP^{4-}] = [\Sigma ATP]\,\frac{K_\alpha}{[H^+] + K_\alpha} \qquad (6.37)$$

Similar manipulations with equations (6.19) and (6.23) lead to

$$[ADP^{2-}] = [\Sigma ADP] \frac{[H^+]}{[H^+] + K_\beta} \tag{6.38}$$

and equations (6.20) and (6.24) give

$$[HPO_4{}^{2-}] = [\Sigma PO_4] \frac{K_\gamma}{[H^+] + K_\gamma} \tag{6.39}$$

Equations (6.37)–(6.39) may then be substituted into (6.34) and we arrive at the relationship

$$K = \frac{[\Sigma ADP][\Sigma PO_4]}{[\Sigma ATP]} \left[\frac{\dfrac{[H^+]}{[H^+] + K_\beta} \dfrac{K_\gamma}{[H^+] + K_\gamma}}{\dfrac{K_\alpha}{[H^+] + K_\alpha}} \right] \tag{6.40}$$

or

$$K = K_\Sigma \left[\frac{\dfrac{[H^+]}{[H^+] + K_\beta} \dfrac{K_\gamma}{[H^+] + K_\gamma}}{\dfrac{K_\alpha}{[H^+] + K_\alpha}} \right] \tag{6.41}$$

We have experimentally evaluated K_Σ at $[H^+] = 10^{-7}$; and we know the values of the ionization constants K_α, K_β, K_γ. Clearly then, K can be computed from the appropriate arithmetic manipulations required by equation (6.41). The result obtained is

$$K = 5.1 \times 10^3 \tag{6.42}$$

and hence $\Delta G°$ for reaction (6.33) is

$$\Delta G° = -6700 \text{ cal mole}^{-1} \tag{6.43}$$

Thus the transfer potential of phosphate from ATP^{4-} to form ADP^{2-} and $HPO_4{}^{2-}$ is significantly different than the phosphate bond energy in the "practical" reaction at pH 7.

Equation (6.41) may also be used in a complementary fashion, to evaluate $\Delta G°'$ (from K_Σ) at pH's other than 7. That this is possible may be understood from the following considerations. The $\Delta G°$ of -6.7 kcal mole^{-1} of equation (6.43) is the free energy change for the chemical reaction of equation (6.33) in which

$$[ATP^{4-}] = 1$$
$$[ADP^{2-}] = 1 \qquad (6.44)$$
$$[HPO_4{}^{2-}] = 1$$

i.e., in which each substance is at unit concentration (assuming activity can be replaced by concentration alone). So long as the standard concentration conditions of each species of equation (6.44) are retained, $\Delta G°$ is -6.7 kcal mole^{-1}, no matter what the pH. At different pH's, the relative amounts of $[ATP^{4-}]$ and $[ATP^{3-}]$ will vary, but if we maintain $[ATP^{4-}]$ at unit concentration it will hydrolyze (to $[ADP^{2-}]$ and $[HPO_4{}^{2-}]$ each at unit concentration) with the same $\Delta G°$ of -6.7 kcal mole^{-1}. Therefore, K of equation (6.42), being directly proportional to $\Delta G°$ of (6.43), will be a *constant* at all pH's.

Keeping this conclusion in mind and looking again at equation (6.41), we see that the left-hand side is a fixed number at all pH's. On the right-hand side, the bracketed factor contains $[H^+]$ and, therefore, has a different value at different pH's. Consequently K_Σ must vary in a compensating manner with change in pH. Therefore $\Delta G°'$ [equation (6.32)] depends on pH, or in other words, the free energy change for the hydrolysis reaction of equation (6.21) varies with pH. That this should be so is not unreasonable since the proportion of ATP^{4-} and ATP^{3-} varies with pH even if $[\Sigma ATP]$ is kept fixed at 1, and ATP^{4-} has a different $\Delta G°$ of hydrolysis than does ATP^{3-}. The actual numerical value of $\Delta G°'$ for reaction (6.21) at different pH's can then be computed from the K_Σ at the corresponding pH, K_Σ being calculated readily from equation (6.41).

3. Thioester Bond Energy

Another example of an experimental evaluation of a group transfer potential using a different approach from that for the phosphate bond energy may be illustrated with CH_3CO—SR. The heats of hydrolysis of a number of thioesters with different R groups have been measured and are all nearly equal

$$CH_3CO\text{—}SR \text{ (l)} + H_2O \text{ (l)} = CH_3COOH \text{ (l)} + HSR \text{ (l)};$$
$$\Delta H_1^\circ \simeq -1 \text{ kcal mole}^{-1} \quad (6.45)$$

Similarly for the corresponding oxygen esters

$$CH_3CO\text{—}OR \text{ (l)} + H_2O \text{ (l)} = CH_3COOH \text{ (l)} + HOR \text{ (l)};$$
$$\Delta H_2^\circ \simeq +1 \text{ kcal mole}^{-1} \quad (6.46)$$

For the first of this pair of reactions we may write

$$\Delta G_1^\circ = \Delta H_1^\circ - T \, \Delta S_1^\circ \quad (6.47)$$

and for the second

$$\Delta G_2^\circ = \Delta H_2^\circ - T \, \Delta S_2^\circ \quad (6.48)$$

so that for equation (6.45) minus equation (6.46)

$$CH_3CO\text{—}SR + ROH = CH_3CO\text{—}OR + RSH \quad (6.49)$$

we obtain

$$\Delta(\Delta G^\circ) = \Delta G_1^\circ - \Delta G_2^\circ$$
$$= (\Delta H_1^\circ - \Delta H_2^\circ) - T(\Delta S_1^\circ - \Delta S_2^\circ) \quad (6.50)$$

Since the species on the left-hand side of equation (6.49) are very similar in molecular arrangement and configuration to the corresponding species on the right-hand side, it is reasonable to assume [see Chapter VIII] that there is no significant overall entropy change in this reaction, that is,

$$\Delta S_1^\circ - \Delta S_2^\circ = 0 \quad (6.51)$$

Therefore,

$$\Delta G_1^\circ = \Delta G_2^\circ + (\Delta H_1^\circ - \Delta H_2^\circ) \quad (6.52)$$

We know ΔH_1° and ΔH_2°.[6] For the ester hydrolysis, ΔG_2° has been experimentally evaluated[7] under a variety of

[6] I. Wadso, *Acta. Chem. Scand.*, **11**, 1745 (1957); *ibid.*, **12**, 630 (1958).

[7] W. P. Jencks, S. Cordes, and J. Carriulo, *J. Biol. Chem.*, **235**, 3608 (1960).

conditions. At pH 7 it is -5.1 kcal mole^{-1}. Hence

$$\Delta G_1° = -5.1 + (-1 - 1) = -7.1 \text{ kcal mole}^{-1} \quad (6.53)$$

Thus, the thioester group has a relatively high transfer potential.

By methods such as these group transfer potentials have been evaluated for a variety of substances. Some "best" values have been assembled in Fig. VI.3. This table may be used in a manner similar to one of redox potentials. Substances high in the list can spontaneously transfer a group to acceptors lower in the list under standard concentration conditions.

Exercises

I. The equilibrium constant for the isomerization reaction

is 56 at 39°C and pH 9.22 [W. P. Jencks, S. Cordes, and J. Carriuolo, *J. Biol. Chem.*, **235**, 3608 (1960)]. Using $\Delta G°$ of hydrolysis of ethyl acetate as a measure of the "bond energy" of oxygen esters, find the transfer potential or "bond energy" of the acetylthioester group.

II. The equilibrium in the hydrolysis of glucose 6-phosphate

$$\text{Glucose-6-P} + H_2O = \text{glucose} + P$$

has been studied by O. Meyerhof and H. Green [*J. Biol. Chem.*, **178**, 655 (1948)]. If the equilibrium constant is expressed in terms of total concentration of each species, Σ,

$$K_{\Sigma} = \frac{[\text{glucose}][\Sigma P]}{[\Sigma G\text{-}6\text{-}P][H_2O]}$$

a value of 122 is found at pH 8.5 and 38°C. What is $\Delta G°$ of the following reaction at pH 8.5 and 38°C?

Necessary ionization constants are listed below.

$$GlcPO_4H^- = GlcPO_4^{2-} + H^+ \qquad K_{\alpha} = 10^{-6.03}$$
$$H_2PO_4^- = HPO_4^{2-} + H^+ \qquad K_{\beta} = 10^{-6.73}$$

Answer: $\Delta G° = -2980$ cal mole^{-1}.

III. The enzyme phosphoglucomutase catalyzes the reaction

As indicated, the 6-phosphate is a mixture of the α and β forms at the 1-position, but the 1-phosphate is pure α. At pH 7 and 25°, the equilibrium constant K for reaction (1) as written is 0.059 [M. R. Atkinson, E. Johnson, and R. K. Morton, *Biochem. J.*, **79**, 12 (1961)]. Let us assume that the equilibrium proportions of α and β forms of the glucose 6-phosphate are the same as in ordinary glucose, for which at equilibrium α is 40% of the total.

Find $\Delta G°$ at pH 7 and 25° for the reaction:

α-D-glucose 6-phosphate = α-D-glucose 1-phosphate   (2)

Answer: $\Delta G° = +1140$ cal mole^{-1}.

IV. The acetyl group transfer potential at 25° and pH 7

in acetyl-coenzyme A, $CH_3CO—S—CH_2CH_2NHR$, can be computed from the following information provided by W. P. Jencks and M. Gilchrist [*J. Am. Chem. Soc.*, **86**, 4657 (1964)]:

$$CH_3\overset{\overset{\displaystyle O}{\|}}{C}—O—CH_2CH_2—N(CH_3)_3{}^+ + H_2O$$

$$= CH_3\overset{\overset{\displaystyle O}{\|}}{C}—OH + HOCH_2CH_2—N(CH_3)_3{}^+ \qquad \Delta G° = 2940 \text{ cal mole}^{-1}$$

$$CH_3\overset{\overset{\displaystyle O}{\|}}{C}—O—CH_2CH_2—N(CH_3)_3{}^+ + HS—CH_2CH_2NHR$$

$$= CH_3\overset{\overset{\displaystyle O}{\|}}{C}—S—CH_2CH_2NHR + HOCH_2CH_2—N(CH_3)_3{}^+ \qquad K = 0.076$$

K_a for CH_3COOH is 1.75×10^{-5}.

What is the "bond energy" of the acetyl-S bond in acetyl-CoA?

V. Heats of reaction for the transfer of methyl groups from a variety of compounds to a common acceptor, homocysteine, have been determined recently by S. H. Mudd, W. A. Klee, and P. D. Ross [*Biochemistry*, **5**, 1653 (1966)], and are tabulated below.

Methyl donor	ΔH (kcal mole^{-1})
$(CH_3)_2S^{\oplus}CH_3$	-6.8
$(CH_3)_2S^{\oplus}CH_2COO^{\ominus}$	-10.6
$(CH_3)_2S^{\oplus}CH_2CH_2COO^{\ominus}$	-8.7
$(CH_3)_2S^{\oplus}CH_2CH_2CHCOO^{\ominus}$	-6.7
$\qquad\qquad\qquad\quad \underset{\displaystyle NH_3{}^{\oplus}}{\mid}$	
$CH_3S^{\oplus}CH_2CH_2CHCOO^{\ominus}$	-13.2
$\underset{\displaystyle 5'\text{-deoxyadenosine}}{\mid} \quad \underset{\displaystyle NH_3{}^{\oplus}}{\mid}$	

The reasonable assumption can be made that $\Delta S°$ for the transfer of CH_3 from one compound to another in this series is near zero. Thus the values of ΔH listed may also serve as good approximations of the methyl group transfer potentials. It would be desirable, however, to check these assumptions, for example, by making an experimental measurement of an equilibrium constant for one of the methyl transfer reactions.

(a) Which pair of substances in the table would seem most suitable for such an experimental measurement?

(b) What value would you predict for the equilibrium constant if you use the data in the table above?

VII. SOME LAWS OF PHYSICOCHEMICAL BEHAVIOR

Part of the aesthetic attractiveness of the theory of energetics lies in its ability to predict a wide variety of scientific laws without any assumptions beyond the two fundamental laws of thermodynamics already described in Chapters I and II. These new principles can be deduced logically from the fundamental laws, most conveniently through the free energy function. We shall not consider the rigorous, logical steps in these derivations, but it is worthwhile to obtain a general idea of the approach used. In this way, one may develop an appreciation of the power of thermodynamic methods in the analysis of physicochemical behavior.

A. Electrochemical Relationships

The primary problem in the thermodynamic analysis of an electrochemical cell is to establish the chemical or physical change which occurs as a result of the flow of current. These details are not always easy to obtain, particularly when liquids of different composition are in contact with each other, as is so often the case in biological systems.

Let us consider a simple cell, such as is shown schematically in Fig. VII.1. An electrode of metal A is dipped into one solution of a salt of A, containing A^+ ions at a concentration C_1. An identical electrode is inserted into the right-hand chamber of the cell containing another solution of the same salt of A but at a concentration C_2. The two liquids are kept separated, but in electrical contact, by means of a suitable porous membrane, or, still better, by an inverted U-tube bridge containing concentrated KCl.

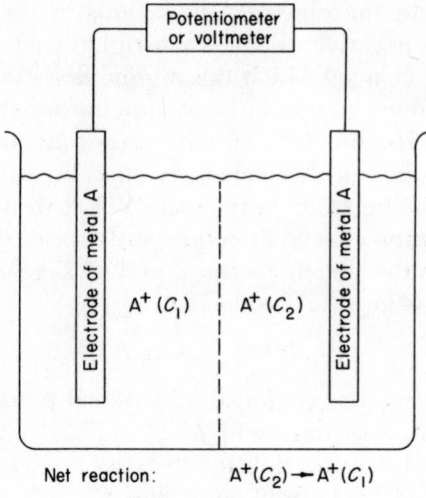

Net reaction: $A^+(C_2) \rightarrow A^+(C_1)$

$$-n\mathcal{F}\mathcal{E} = \Delta G = RT \ln(C_1/C_2)$$

FIG. VII.1. Electrochemical cell: concentration type.

We must now determine the chemical changes which would occur if one mole of electrons of current were to flow through the circuit. The electron current can be assumed to flow from left to right, or right to left; for our analysis it does not matter. We shall adopt the common convention, therefore, of considering the electrons to flow in the outer circuit, through the potentiometer, from left to right. For this to occur, electrons must be produced at the left-hand electrode; they can be liberated from the metal in the reaction

$$A \rightarrow A^+(C_1) + e \tag{7.1}$$

These electrons could then flow through the potentiometer toward the right-hand electrode; here they would have to be absorbed, or they would pile up on the metal and produce an enormous electrostatic repulsion. The absorption reaction is

$$e + A^+(C_2) \rightarrow A \tag{7.2}$$

To complete the electrical flow, ions in the solutions must carry negative charge from right to left. The concentration changes which these ionic flows produce are often complex, particularly at junctions between different liquids, but in a suitable experimental arrangement the effect of these changes upon the net chemical reaction can be made very small. We shall neglect any liquid-junction effects, therefore, and assume that the net reaction in the electrochemical cell of Fig. VII.1 is the sum of equations (7.1) and (7.2):

$$A^+(C_2) \to A^+(C_1) \tag{7.3}$$

As for any other chemical or physical transformation, there is a ΔG associated with reaction (7.3). In view of the fact that this net reaction involves merely changing the concentration of A^+ from one value, C_2, to another C_1, it is evident that we can relate ΔG to the concentrations by means of a relation similar to (5.3):

$$\Delta G = RT \ln \frac{C_1}{C_2} \tag{7.4}$$

In addition, ΔG originally acquired the name "free energy" change because it is also a measure of the maximum useful work which can be obtained from a reaction. More precisely,

$$\Delta G = -W_{max} \tag{7.5}$$

In our present problem this work is electrical in nature, so we may also write

$$W_{max} = \text{charge} \times \text{potential} \\ = q \times \mathscr{E} \tag{7.6}$$

The charge carried by one mole of electrons is 96,500 coulombs, usually abbreviated by the symbol $\mathscr{F}$ (the Faraday), so we may write

$$W_{max} = \mathscr{F}\mathscr{E} \tag{7.7}$$

To generalize just a little further, let us also include cases where the number of moles of electrons, n, might be more, or less, than one, and write

$$W_{max} = n\mathscr{F}\mathscr{E} \tag{7.8}$$

It follows from equations (7.5) and (7.8) that

$$\Delta G = -n\mathscr{F}\mathscr{E} \tag{7.9}$$

Consequently, since ΔG of equation (7.9) refers to the same chemical change [reaction (7.3)] as does ΔG of equation (7.4), the two are the same thing, and

$$-n\mathscr{F}\mathscr{E} = RT \ln \frac{C_1}{C_2} \tag{7.10}$$

or

$$\mathscr{E} = -\frac{RT}{n\mathscr{F}} \ln \frac{C_1}{C_2} = \frac{RT}{n\mathscr{F}} \ln \frac{C_2}{C_1} \tag{7.11}$$

If, for example, A^+ were Na^+ ion, we may write specifically

$$\mathscr{E} = \frac{RT}{n\mathscr{F}} \ln \frac{[Na^+]_2}{[Na^+]_1} \tag{7.12}$$

Thus we arrive at the well-known Nernst equation for electrochemical potentials in this example for a concentration cell. The same general procedure may be used for the derivation of equations for the electromotive force of more complicated electrochemical systems. In every case it is necessary first to write the net chemical or physical transformation that occurs in the cell, secondly to formulate the appropriate expression for ΔG for this transformation, and thirdly to equate this ΔG to the electrical work. Simple algebraic manipulation will lead to the equation for $\mathscr{E}$.

B. Osmotic Pressure

In analyzing the thermodynamic basis of osmotic phenomena, we shall also find it convenient to visualize an appropriate idealized system such as is shown in Fig. VII.2. The two arms of a U-tube, separated by a partition consisting of a membrane permeable to the solvent but not to the solute (dashed line in Fig. VII.2),

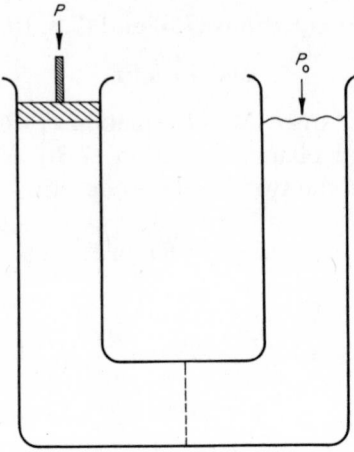

FIG. VII.2. Osmotic pressure.

are first filled with pure solvent to equal heights in both arms. Under these conditions, and with the pressure P the same as the atmospheric pressure P_0 and the temperature constant, the system is at equilibrium. Hence

$$\Delta G = 0 = G_{\text{right}} - G_{\text{left}} \qquad (7.13)$$

or the chemical potential of solvent on the right is equal to that on the left.

Now we add some solute to the left-hand side. The presence of dissolved solute lowers the chemical potential of the solvent by an amount proportional to the number of moles of added solute, n_2:

Lowering of G of solvent due to solute $= RTn_2$ $\quad(7.14)$[1]

In the absence of any other stress, solvent would move from the right side of the tube to the left, since that on

[1] We shall accept this relation without proof.

the right retains its initial higher chemical potential. Such a flow could be prevented, however, by increasing the chemical potential of the solvent on the left; for example, by making the pressure P greater than the atmospheric pressure, P_0:

Increase of G of solvent due to
$$\text{increased pressure} = V(P - P_0) \quad (7.15)^2$$

In this equation, V is the volume of solvent on the left side of the U-tube. If the increase in G due to the extra pressure exerted just balances the decrease due to added solute, then equilibrium will be re-established, no solvent will flow from one side to the other, and we may equate (7.14) and (7.15).

$$V(P - P_0) = RTn_2 \quad (7.16)$$

This increase in pressure necessary to maintain equilibrium in the presence of added solute is named the osmotic pressure, π:

$$\pi = P - P_0 \quad (7.17)$$

Making use of equation (7.17) and rearranging (7.16) we obtain the familiar form

$$\pi = RTn_2/V = RTC_2 \quad (7.18)$$

where C_2 is the number of moles per liter of dissolved solute.

Since π depends on C_2, if we can measure the osmotic pressure, we can calculate C_2 in moles (per liter). Thus, osmotic pressure measurements provide a means of obtaining the molecular weight of a solute. In practice this method is particularly useful for macromolecules.

C. Molecular Weight from Ultracentrifugation

One of the earliest of the physicochemical properties that one wishes to know about a biological macromolecule is its molecular weight. Ultracentrifugation is

---

[2] We shall accept this relation without proof.

perhaps the most versatile method for obtaining such weights.

The ultracentrifuge may be used in several different ways to obtain molecular weights. One of these procedures is known as *sedimentation equilibrium*. A solution is placed in a small cell which in turn is set in a rotor [Fig.VII.3 (A)]. The rotor is then rotated at high speed

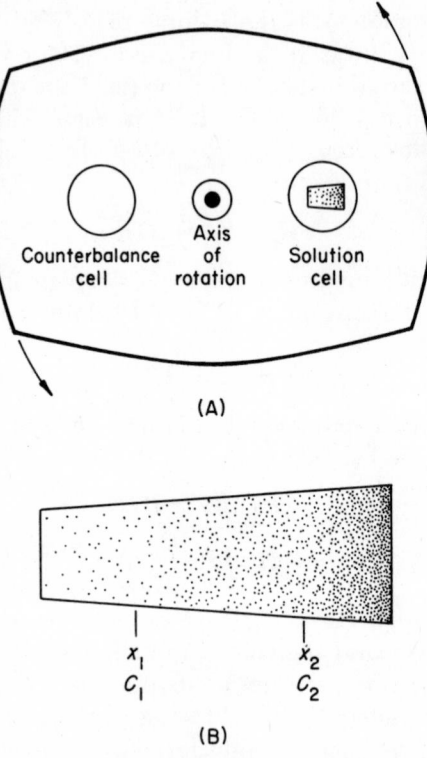

(A)

(B)

FIG. VII.3. Sedimentation equilibrium.

($\sim 15{,}000$ revolutions per minute) so that a strong centrifugal force is produced which tends to move the molecules toward the outer end of the cell [Fig. VII.3 (B)]. As the molecules congregate at the right side of the cell, their concentration increases, but in turn the concentration of those remaining at the left is diminished. As a result, a *diffusional force* is set up, opposite in direction to the centrifugal force, which tends to move molecules back from right to left. Ultimately the centrifugal and diffusional forces balance exactly and equilibrium is established in which a definite concentration gradient, increasing from left to right, exists in the cell indefinitely. At this stage, the concentrations C_1 and C_2 are measured at two points in the cell at distances x_1 and x_2 from the center of the rotor. From this information, usually obtained by optical means, and the following theoretical analysis, one can compute the molecular weight.

Since the concentrations C_1 and C_2 differ, there must be a difference in free energy between x_1 and x_2 due to this concentration gradient. We can compute this ΔG readily from equation (5.1), in the same way as we have just obtained equation (7.4):

$$\Delta G_{conc} = G_1(\text{at } x_1) - G_2(\text{at } x_2) = RT \ln C_1 - RT \ln C_2$$
$$= RT \ln (C_1/C_2) \quad (7.19)$$

Since C_1 is less than C_2, C_1/C_2 will be less than unity, its logarithm will be negative and hence ΔG will be negative. It follows, therefore, that molecules ought to move back spontaneously from position x_2 to x_1. We know they do not do so. Evidently the concentrational ΔG must be exactly balanced by a free energy change between x_1 and x_2 due to the centrifugal field.

This $\Delta G_{centrifugal}$ is readily obtained from the relationship between free energy and maximum work, as was the case with the electrochemical problem above. To move an object of mass M against a centrifugal force (due to an acceleration of $\omega^2 x$) from point x_2 to x_1 requires an amount of work

$$W = \tfrac{1}{2}M\omega^2(x_1{}^2 - x_2{}^2) \quad (7.20)[3]$$

[3] We shall accept this relation without proof.

where ω is the angular velocity of the rotor. If the object is in a solvent, its effective mass will not be M, but will be less because of a buoyancy correction. This correction, as one may recall from Archimedes' principle, is the weight of the medium displaced by the solute. If one knows the volume of 1 gm of solute, v, then $v\rho$, where ρ is the density of the solution, gives the weight of solvent displaced by 1 gm of solute. If $v\rho$ approaches unity, then the effective mass of the solute reaches zero, and the solute will float in the solvent no matter how strong the centrifugal field. Thus it should become apparent that with a buoyancy correction, the centrifugal work is given by

$$W = \tfrac{1}{2}M(1 - v\rho)\omega^2(x_1^2 - x_2^2) \qquad (7.21)$$

Returning then to our conclusion that

$$\Delta G_{conc} + \Delta G_{cent} = 0 \qquad (7.22)$$

and reminding ourselves of equation (7.5), we may write

$$RT \ln (C_1/C_2) = \tfrac{1}{2}M(1 - v\rho)\omega^2(x_1^2 - x_2^2) \qquad (7.23)$$

Thus for an explicit equation for the molecular weight, we obtain

$$M = \frac{2RT \ln (C_1/C_2)}{(1 - v\rho)\omega^2(x_2^2 - x_1^2)} \qquad (7.24)$$

We have thus derived laws of physicochemical behavior for electrochemical cells, osmotic pressure, and sedimentation. In each case our procedure was to consider the balancing free energies which are involved in a given system. For each type of free energy we obtained a relationship between ΔG and experimentally measurable quantities. Thus we found equations relating ΔG to concentration differences, electric potentials, pressure differences, and centrifugal fields. Equating these relationships for corresponding balancing

ΔG's, we obtained a new equation which must govern the behavior of the system considered.

There are also relationships, which we have not considered, between ΔG and temperature, surface properties, tension, magnetic properties, etc. It should thus be evident that from simply the two basic laws of thermodynamics, through the concept of free energy, we can derive a host of principles which govern the behavior of matter.

VIII. ENERGETICS FROM A MOLECULAR-STATISTICAL VIEWPOINT

In classical energetics we derive a series of relationships, based on the two fundamental laws of thermodynamics, which correlate particular thermodynamic functions (e.g., the chemical potential) with experimentally measurable properties of matter in bulk (e.g., the equilibrium constant). Since the establishment of the laws of thermodynamics about a century ago, our understanding of the properties of matter in bulk from the atomic standpoint has developed immensely. We might reasonably expect, therefore, that it should be possible to express thermodynamic functions in terms of atomic and molecular properties. It is this combination of specific molecular models with certain theorems of statistics governing the behavior of large assemblies of individual molecules that makes up the branch of energetics frequently named *statistical thermodynamics*.

A. Fundamental Assumptions

1. Molecular

One fundamental axiom of statistical energetics is that matter is constituted of atoms. Implicit in this assumption are all the attributes and properties which we associate with atoms and molecules. Some of these details, such as the internal constitution of atoms, can be ignored for our present purposes. Others, particularly the quantum characteristics of molecular systems, must be examined more carefully.

The basic principle of quantum theory is that the en-

Electron orbits

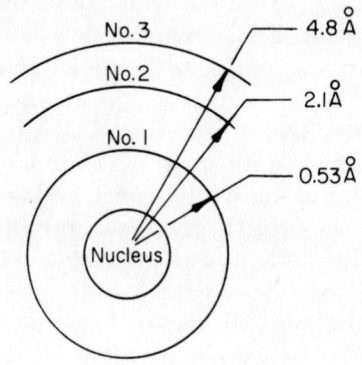

Energy levels

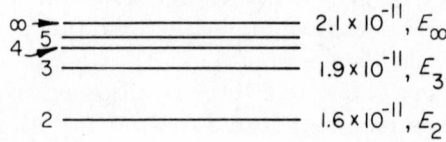

Orbit number   Relative energy (ergs)

FIG. VIII.1. Energy levels in a hydrogen atom.

ergy of an atom or molecule cannot vary continuously but may possess only certain discrete, very sharp, or *quantized* values. Thus, if the energy levels of a particular atom are E_1, E_2, and E_3 (Fig. VIII.1), the atom can never possess an energy between E_1 and E_2 or between E_2 and E_3. The quantum assumption cannot be derived from the classical mechanics of moving objects as applied to moving atoms; it is a completely independent axiom which must be added to classical atomic and molecular theory. Its justification lies, as does that of all other fundamental scientific axioms, in the great power it has given us in the understanding of known behavior and the prediction of new and unsuspected aspects of natural phenomena.

Usually, the student is first introduced to the quantum concept in connection with atomic spectra. The interaction of radiation with matter to produce discrete line spectra can be explained in terms of transitions of an electron from one energy level in an atom to another (Fig. VIII.1). For a first approximation, we may associate each energy level with an orbit of an electron's motion around the nucleus. For simplicity, we may consider the hydrogen atom, with only a single electron (Fig. VIII.1). In its lowest energy state, the "ground state," the hydrogen atom has its electron in orbit 1. If radiation of sufficient energy (1.6×10^{-11} erg) is absorbed by the atom, the electron may be boosted to orbit 2. With absorption of 1.9×10^{-11} erg of energy, the electron may jump from the lowest level to orbit number 3. There exist an infinite number of orbits, but the energy spacing between successive ones becomes smaller and smaller as we go up the scale. If an energy slightly greater than 2.1×10^{-11} erg is imparted to the atom, then the electron is actually separated from the hydrogen nucleus, and a positively charged hydrogen ion is left. Hence, the energy difference between orbits 1 and ∞ is named the *ionization energy*. For our purposes, the main point to be noticed in Fig. VIII.1 is that there is no energy level between, for example, 0 and 1.6×10^{-11} erg, and that, therefore, hydrogen atoms cannot absorb radiation with an energy of, for example, 1×10^{-11} erg in each quantum.

In molecules, too, there are different energy levels due

to the displacement of an electron from a lower to a higher orbit. The spacings between these energy levels is also of the order of magnitude of 10^{-11} erg. In molecules, furthermore, there are other forms of motion, some of which are not present in atoms (Fig. VIII.2), and with each of these motions there is an associated energy.

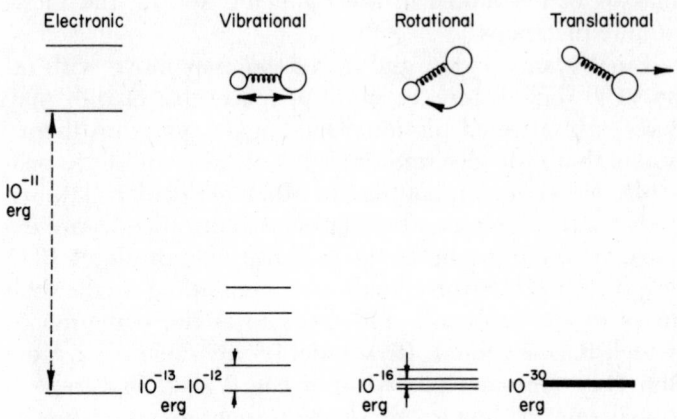

FIG. VIII.2. Energy levels in a molecule.

Two connected atoms in a molecule are joined by a valence bond which may be visualized as a spring. The two atoms thus are capable of vibrating toward and away from each other. The frequency of this vibration depends on the energy imparted to the vibrating atoms. In intramolecular vibrational motions, as in electron displacements, the energies cannot be any value, but must be only certain discrete values (Fig. VIII.2). The spacing between vibrational energy levels, however, is smaller than between electronic levels, the former being of the order of magnitude of 10^{-13} to 10^{-12} erg. The vibrational energies that are permissible in any given case depend on the structure of the molecule. In general, the spacing between energy levels is larger the greater is the force of attraction between the vibrating atoms and the smaller are the masses of the atoms.

In addition to vibrational motion, a molecule may be involved in rotational motions which again have only certain discrete energies associated with them (Fig. VIII.2). Rotational energies are even smaller than vibrational, being of the order of magnitude of 10^{-16} erg. The spacing between these levels in general depends on the masses of the atoms in the molecule and on the interatomic distances.

Finally, molecules, and atoms too, may move with respect to some reference point in space; that is, they may have translational motion. Once again quantum theory states that only discrete energies of translation are possible. However, in contrast to other molecular motions, the spacings between translational energy levels are extremely small, being of the order of magnitude of 10^{-30} erg (Fig. VIII.2), the actual value depending on the total mass of the molecule and the size of the container in which it is confined. It is undoubtedly clear even from the very schematic drawing of Fig. VIII.2 that translational energy levels are so close together, they practically merge into a continuum of energy. In fact, for most practical purposes, they can be treated as a continuum; that is, we may ignore the quantization of translational motion. As a consequence it can be shown that the average energy of translation of a mole of particles depends only on the temperature and is the same for all molecules or atoms:

$$E_{\text{translation}} = \tfrac{3}{2}RT \quad \text{(per mole)} \tag{8.1}$$

2. Statistical

We have outlined the various types of energy levels which may exist in a molecule. In a group of molecules of a single substance, not every molecule has exactly the same energy despite the fact that each molecule has available to it exactly the same energy levels. For example, if we consider the very simple energy level diagram

of Fig. VIII.3 A to be characteristic of some given molecular structure, and if we have a group of 10 molecules of
this substance to which we give 10 units of energy, it is
exceedingly unlikely that all of the molecules will be in
the second energy level at the same time (Fig. VIII.3 B).

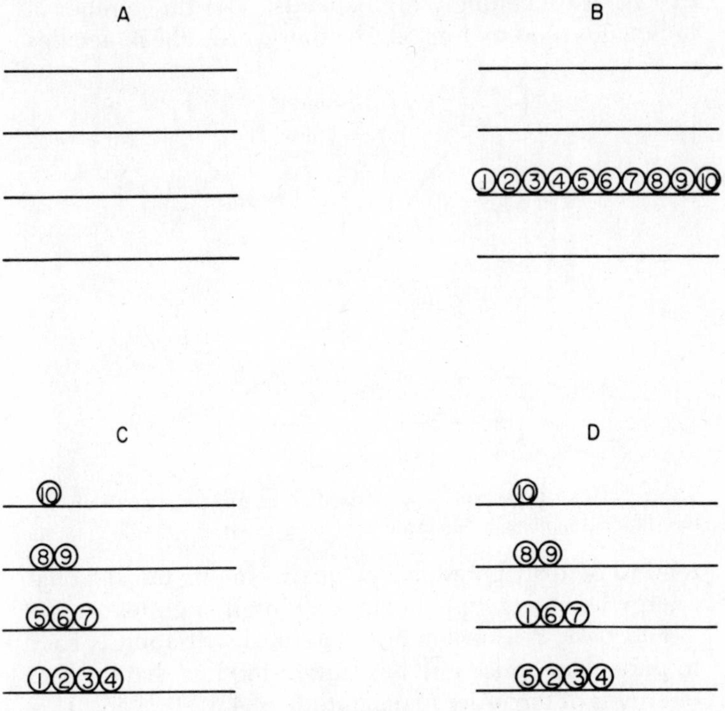

FIG. VIII.3. Distribution of molecules among energy levels.

Rather the molecules will be distributed among the energy levels in some unsymmetrical fashion consistent
with the possession of a total energy of 10 units (Fig.
VIII.3 C), the particular form of the distribution depending on the kind of energy level being considered.

For example, with respect to translational motion along
any one direction in space (e.g., along the x-axis of the
container), a very wide spectrum of energies is possible

(Fig. VIII.4). A certain number of molecules are in the very lowest level; essentially an equal number are in the second level, in the third level, etc. In fact, the number of molecules in the millionth translational level is nearly the same as in the very first. Only in much higher levels, that is, at exceedingly high speeds, does the number of molecules tend to drop off. In other words, the molecules

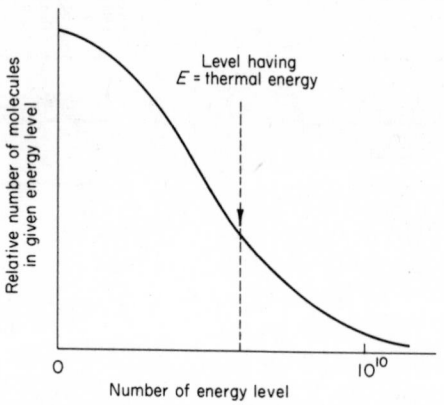

FIG. VIII.4. Distribution of molecules among energy levels for translational motion in one direction (along x-axis).

tend to be distributed fairly equally among translational energy levels, except at extremely high energies.

The basic reason for this type of distribution is easy to understand once one is aware of the fact that thermal energy is of the order of magnitude of 4×10^{-14} erg. This quantity is very large compared to the spacing between translational energy levels (Fig. VIII.2). Thus many molecules can be in high translational states, as well as in low ones. Only for exceedingly high speeds is thermal energy insufficient to supply the required translational energy to more than a few molecules.

In fact, this argument can easily be put into quantitative terms. Suppose some molecules are at equilibrium in their distribution between two levels with energies of E' and E'' (in calories per mole). Let the number of molecules in each level at equilibrium be represented by n' and n'', respectively. Then the equilibrium constant,

$$K = n''/n' \qquad (8.2)$$

may be inserted into equation (4.1) to give

$$\Delta G° = -RT \ln (n''/n') \qquad (8.3)$$

From equation (3.5) we obtain a replacement for $\Delta G°$:

$$\Delta E° - T \Delta S° = -RT \ln (n''/n') \qquad (8.4)$$

If the two energy levels E' and E'' have no intrinsic preference, one over the other, for the molecules, then the intrinsic probability of the molecules being in level E' is the same as that of being in level E''. Under these circumstances as we shall show in Section B, S'' and S', the entropies of the molecules in these levels are the same, and hence $\Delta S° = 0$. Thus rearranging equation (7.4) to the exponential form we obtain[1]

$$\frac{n''}{n'} = \exp\left(-\frac{\Delta E°}{RT}\right) = \exp\left[-\frac{(E'' - E')}{RT}\right] \qquad (8.5)$$

The larger the difference $(E'' - E')$, the smaller will be the right hand side of equation (8.5) and hence the smaller the number of molecules n'' in the higher energy level, relative to n'. Figure VIII.4 shows in essence a graphical representation of this distribution of molecules among energy levels for translational motion. If we consider energy per molecule, ϵ, instead of per mole, E, we can modify equation (8.5) slightly to read

$$\frac{n''}{n'} = \exp\left[-\frac{(E'' - E')/N}{RT/N}\right] = \exp\left(-\frac{\Delta \epsilon}{kT}\right) \qquad (8.6)$$

where N is Avogadro's number, and $k = R/N$ is called the Boltzmann constant in recognition of the discoverer

[1] $e^{x(y+z)} = \exp [x(y + z)]$.

of this distribution equation, the Boltzmann equation. Thermal energy is defined as RT (per mole) or kT (per molecule) and thus equals approximately 0.6 kcal mole^{-1} or 4×10^{-14} erg per molecule at room temperature.

For translational motion $\epsilon_2 - \epsilon_1$ between the first and second successive levels is very small, ca. 10^{-30} erg. Clearly $\Delta\epsilon/kT$ is a very small number and the exponential term on the right-hand side of equation (8.6) is essentially unity. Thus n_2 the number of molecules in the second level is essentially the same as n_1. Only for the billionth energy level does $\epsilon_{10^9} - \epsilon_1$ become appreciable compared to kT and only then does n_{10^9}/n_1 begin to drop appreciably below 1.

Likewise, with respect to rotational motion, some molecules occupy the lower energy levels, others the higher. Here again thermal energy, 4×10^{-14} erg, is relatively large compared to the spacing between energy levels, 10^{-16} erg, and hence the molecules are distributed not too disproportionately among the energy states.

In contrast, in vibrational motion, where the spacing between levels increases in magnitude to around 10^{-13} erg, most of the molecules, if at room temperature and not excited by illumination, tend to be in the lowest energy level, with only a few in higher energy levels. Such a heavily slanted distribution arises from the fact that in the absence of radiation, again only thermal energy is available to excite molecules. A few molecules may be able to accumulate somewhat more than this quantity of energy at room temperature, but the overwhelming mass of them will be near this average. It is clear from Fig. VIII.2 that while 4×10^{-14} erg is enough to put a molecule in a high translational or rotational level, it is insufficient to raise a molecule very high in the vibrational scale. Similar conclusions can be reached from the Boltzmann law, equation (8.6). Likewise, it is immediately obvious from Fig. VIII.2 or from the Boltzmann equation that all the molecules will be in the lowest electronic energy state since thermal energy is several orders of magnitude too small to supply the 10^{-11} erg necessary to excite an electron to an orbit above the ground state.

Except for the electronic energy level, a particular molecule is unlikely to stay in a given energy level very long. Collisions occur constantly between molecules, with accompanying exchanges of energy, and as a result transitions from one energy level to another are constantly in progress, even for a system in equilibrium. For a system in equilibrium containing a large number of molecules, there will be a definite average apportioning of molecules among the different energy levels. Although different molecules may occupy different levels at different times, on the average a particular level will have the same number of tenants. It should be clear, nevertheless, that a particular average distribution can be obtained in many different ways depending on which individual molecules of the group happen to be residing in each energy level. For example, in connection with the energy levels of Fig. VIII.3, a distribution of four molecules in the lowest level, three in the second, two in the third and one in the fourth can be obtained as shown in Fig. VIII.3 C; it can also be obtained, with one rearrangement, in the alternative fashion shown in Fig. VIII.3 D; and many other permutations can be written down readily.

Every molecular structure has a definite set of energy levels corresponding to it. For example, if we have a large collection of hydrogens and carbons in the ratio of four carbon atoms to ten hydrogen atoms, these may combine to form molecules of normal butane (I) which have a set of levels such as shown in Fig. VIII.5. The same atoms combined to form an alternative structure, isobutane (II), have a different set of energy levels (Fig. VIII.5). The problem that we wish to consider is, which configuration will be preferred by the molecules; that is,

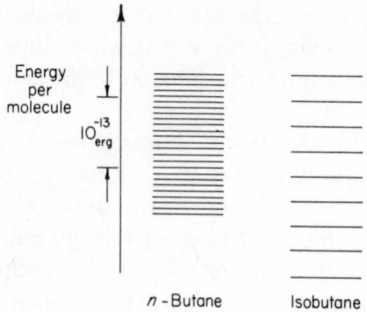

FIG. VIII.5. Statistical and energetic factors contributing to molecular stability.

which molecular structure, (I) or (II), is more probable.

$$
\begin{array}{cccc}
& H & H & H & H \\
& | & | & | & | \\
H-& C-& C-& C-& C-H \\
& | & | & | & | \\
& H & H & H & H
\end{array}
$$

(I)

$$
\begin{array}{ccc}
& H & H & H \\
& | & | & | \\
H-& C-& C-& C-H \\
& | & & | \\
& H & & H \\
& & H-C-H \\
& & | \\
& & H
\end{array}
$$

(II)

Before elaborating on this problem, let us consider an analogous but more familiar probability question. For theoretical or practical purposes we might wish to know which sum is most likely to appear in a single toss of two (perfectly balanced) dice. Without going into any of the theorems of probability, we could answer this question simply by making a list of each of the possible sums which can be obtained (Table VIII.1) and then enumerating for each entry all the possible ways in which this number can be thrown. For example, there is only one way in which the sum 2 can be thrown, that is, by having 1 appear on both dice. In contrast, there are three different distributions (see Table VIII.1) which lead to number 4. If we continue to list the individual arrangements of the two dice which can lead to each sum, we find

TABLE VIII.1
STATISTICS OF DICE

Sum for single throw	Individual arrangements giving sum		Total ways of obtaining sum
	Die No. 1	Die No. 2	
2	1	1	1
3	1	2	2
	2	1	
4	1	3	3
	2	2	
	3	1	
5	1	4	4
	2	3	
	3	2	
	4	1	
6	1	5	5
	2	4	
	3	3	
	4	2	
	5	1	
7	1	6	6
	2	5	
	3	4	
	4	3	
	5	2	
	6	1	
8	2	6	5
	3	5	
	4	4	
	5	3	
	6	2	
9	3	6	4
	4	5	
	5	4	
	6	3	

TABLE VIII.1 (*Continued*)

Sum for single throw	Individual arrangements giving sum		Total ways of obtaining sum
	Die No. 1	Die No. 2	
10	4	6	3
	5	5	
	6	4	
11	5	6	2
	6	5	
12	6	6	1

quickly that the largest number of arrangements can be made for the number 7. Hence the number 7 is the most probable one, the one most likely to appear.

The basic postulate of molecular statistics is similar in nature to that in the throwing of dice. In essence it says that if we have two different sets of energy levels, starting at the same ground state, one set corresponding to one molecular structure and the second to an alternative structure, then the atoms will tend to arrange themselves into the molecular structure which has available to it the larger number of energy levels. The more energy levels available in a given set to the assembly of molecules, the larger is the number of ways in which the molecules can be distributed among the levels. The larger the number of different ways of distributing the molecules, the more probable is the structure which corresponds to that set of energy levels. For example, the energy levels of normal butane are much mose closely spaced than those of isobutane (Fig. VIII.5). Consequently, from probability considerations alone, C_4H_{10} is more likely to be in the form of n-butane than isobutane.

B. Relationship to Thermodynamic Quantities

The properties of the butane system also point up the one additional factor which we must not forget in applying the reasoning of molecular statistics. Although statistical considerations emphasize the stabilization provided by a high density of energy levels, we must not discard entirely the classical mechanical viewpoint that a system tends toward the state of minimum internal energy. Thus, as shown in Fig. VIII.5 the ground state of isobutane is lower in energy than the ground state of n-butane; when each molecule is in a state of rest, the various attractive and repulsive interactions between the four carbon and ten hydrogen atoms leads to a state of lower energy for the isobutane configuration than for normal butane. As a result there is a pull toward the isobutane structure due to energetic factors which can counteract in part the tendency toward the normal butane structure favored by probability effects.

The counteracting effects of energy and probability factors can be demonstrated even on a microscopic scale. If, for example, 500 white balls and 500 red balls are placed in a box and shaken vigorously, then the chances are very high that the bottom layer will have approximately as many white balls as red ones. If, however, the red balls have small pieces of iron in them and a large magnet is placed below the bottom of the box, then after vigorous shaking one will find many more red balls than white balls in the bottom layer. Thus the "striving" toward a distribution of maximum probability is counteracted by a tendency to reach a state of lower energy.[2]

It becomes clear, then, that the net result will depend on the relative magnitude of these two effects, which, for molecular systems, we wish to express in quantitative terms.

Since the net result of the counterbalancing of the energetic and statistical factors is a measure of the tendency toward formation of one molecular structure from some other, the resultant quantity obviously has the

---

[2] Likewise in weighted dice, the intrinsic probability factor is counterbalanced by the tendency of the dice to attain minimum gravitational energy.

characteristics of the chemical potential. Thus, it should seem reasonable that statistical energetics leads one to the relation

$$\Delta G = \text{(Change in ground-state energy)}$$
$$- \text{(Change in probability of system)} \quad (8.7)$$

One need only to recall that a transformation can occur spontaneously when ΔG is negative. ΔG can be negative, according to equation (8.7), under either of two circumstances: (1) if the change in energy in the ground state, ΔE_0, is negative, that is, the energy drops, or (2) if the probability of the configurations is greater at the end than at the outset. A negative sign must precede the probability term in (8.7), for an increase in probability favors a reaction, that is, should lead to a *negative* value for ΔG.

More specifically, statistical thermodynamics leads to an equation of the following type in place of (8.7)

$$\Delta G = \Delta E_0 - RT \ln Z \quad (8.8)$$

where Z is a measure of the relative probability of the configuration of the products of the reaction as compared to the reactants.

It is instructive at this point to recall equation (3.5):

$$\Delta G = \Delta E - T \, \Delta S \quad (8.9)$$

The first terms on the right-hand side of (8.8) and (8.9) are not exactly the same since in (8.8) ΔE_0 is the change in internal energy when the molecules are essentially without any motion, that is, at the absolute zero of temperature, whereas in (8.9) ΔE refers to the change in internal energy at the temperature of the reaction. However, in our present qualitative discussion this distinction may be neglected. In consequence we see from a comparison of the second terms that

$$\Delta S = R \ln Z \quad (8.10)$$

In other words, from the molecular-statistical viewpoint,

it is the entropy change which is related to the relative probability. An increase in probability of the system thus is the molecular basis for an increase in entropy. From the atomic theory, therefore, we are able to obtain a mechanical interpretation for the abstract concept of entropy originally introduced in classical energetics.

C. Some Applications

It remains for us to consider briefly what molecular structural factors lead to increased probabilities, increased entropies, and hence negative ΔG's. We should recall that these probabilities are determined by the density in energy levels, that is, by the closeness of their spacing. The energy levels, in turn, are determined by molecular motions. In a general way, one can say that the greater the freedom of motion, the closer are the energy levels; contrariwise, any restraints on the movement of the molecules or any interference with the freedom of motion within the molecule increases the spacing between energy levels. The significance of these general statements can be made more evident if we consider a few examples.

A particularly simple case is the melting of ice:

$$H_2O \text{ (crystals)} \rightarrow H_2O \text{ (liquid)} \qquad (8.11)$$

As we are all aware, this process proceeds spontaneously to the right if the temperature is a fraction of a degree above 0°C. From energy considerations alone, such a transformation would be an anomaly since it requires an input of energy, approximately 1400 cal mole^{-1} (Fig. VIII.6). From a molecular-statistical viewpoint, however, it is immediately evident that H_2O molecules in water have much greater freedom of motion than they do in ice. Consequently the factor Z, the measure of the relative probability of the liquid configuration to the crystalline, is greater than unity, and hence ΔS is positive.

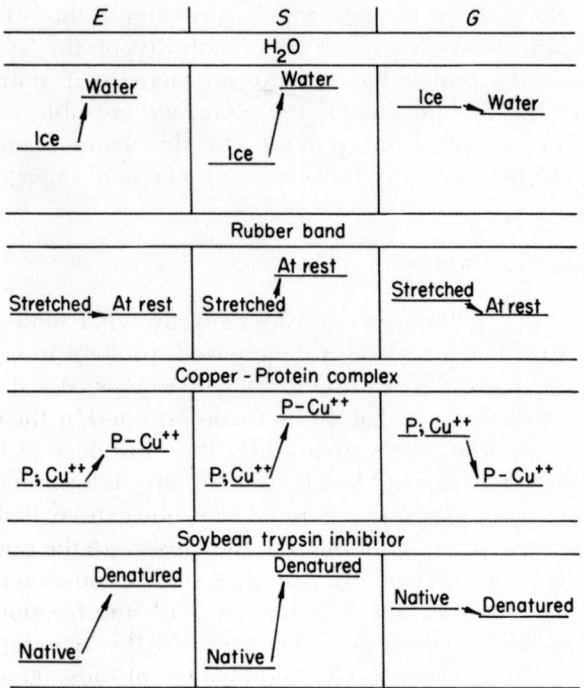

FIG. VIII.6. Some processes which occur spontaneously despite unfavorable changes in internal energy.

It is this increase in entropy (Fig. VIII.6) which (when multiplied by T) more than compensates for ΔE and hence leads (equation 8.9) to a drop in free energy, as one would expect for a spontaneous process.

For water in its various states—gas, liquid, solid— the corresponding entropies have been determined experimentally (Table VIII.2). As one would expect, the entropy increases in the order solid < liquid < gas, paralleling the increase in freedom of motion of the molecules. Similarly the entropy increases with increasing softness of a metal (TableVIII.2), i.e., with increasing ease of separation of atoms even in the solid state. Likewise entropy increases with increasing molec-

TABLE VIII.2

ENTROPY AND MOLECULAR DISORDER

Entropy and Physical State: H_2O at 0°C

State	Entropy[a]
Ice	9.8
Liquid	15
Vapor (1 atm)	45

Entropy and Hardness

Element	Entropy[a]	Hardness
C (diamond)	0.6	10
B	1.4	9.5
Si	4.5	7
Cu	8.0	2.7
Ca	10.0	1.5
Na	12.2	0.5

Entropy and Molecular Complexity and Molecular Weight:
Gaseous Molecules at 1 Atm and 25°C

Molecule	Molecular weight	Entropy[a]
Monatomic		
H	1	27
He	4	30
A	40	37
Xe	131	41
Polyatomic		
H_2	2	31
N_2	28	46
I_2	254	63
H_2O	18	45
H_2S	34	49
CO_2	44	51
NH_3	17	46
CH_4	16	44
CCl_4	154	74

[a] Cal mole^{-1} deg^{-1}.

58423

ular weight and with increasing complexity of a molecule (Table VIII.2). Thus, even for monatomic gases, which have no rotational or vibrational motions (Figure VIII.2), the density of translational energy levels increases, because the spacing between these levels decreases with increasing molecular weight. Consequently the entropy of argon is well above that for helium. In the polyatomic molecules, energy levels appear due to vibrations and rotations, and the number of levels increases with the number of atoms in the molecule and with their weight. Thus, the entropy increases in a parallel fashion (see Table VIII.2).

In principle, it should be possible to compute the absolute entropy of a substance if one knows full details about its molecular structure and motions. In practice, these calculations are difficult and often intractable. A simple example may illustrate one feature of such quantitative calculations.

We start with equation (8.10). For molecular-statistical calculations, the relative probability Z is defined in a different manner than in common statistical calculations, where Z varies only between zero and unity. In molecular statistics, the probability Z is measured by the total number of different arrangements that a molecular system may be placed into. For example, at temperatures approaching absolute zero, the molecules in a crystalline substance such as solid HCl lose their various twistings and vibrations, drop to their lowest available energy level and settle down into a perfect crystalline pattern, schematically represented by

HCl HCl HCl HCl . . .

Under these circumstances there exists *only one* possible arrangement of the molecules in the crystal. Therefore Z is unity, and it follows from equation (8.10) that the entropy of crystalline HCl at 0°K is zero.

The molecules of CO in the crystalline state also lose

their molecular vibrations and twistings as $T \to 0°K$, and they too settle down into their lowest energy level. In this case, however, it turns out that the crystal does not attain a perfect array. Because the C and O atoms are nearly equal in size, as the temperature approaches $0°K$, the molecules can settle into the lattice lined up either as CO or as OC. Thus the crystalline pattern may be represented schematically as

$$\text{CO CO OC CO . . .}$$

Obviously there are two possible arrangements for each CO molecule; the value of Z becomes 2. One would compute, therefore, from equation (8.10) an entropy of $R \ln 2 = 1.38$ (cal mole^{-1} deg^{-1}) for crystalline carbon monoxide at $0°K$. The calculated value agrees closely with the experimentally measured one of 1.1 (cal mole^{-1} deg^{-1}).

In the example of ice $\to$ water described above, the direction of the entropy change is immediately obvious from visible macroscopic properties of the substance. Even more interesting are those cases where no simple macroscopic observation reflects the molecular state and where, in consequence, a molecular statistical analysis provides some insight into configurational changes at the molecular level.

From common experience we know that a stretched rubber band can snap back spontaneously to the rest position. Clearly then ΔG must be negative for this process (Fig. VIII.6):

rubber band (stretched) $\to$ rubber band (at rest);
$$\Delta G < 0 \quad (8.12)$$

Experimental measurements show, however, that ΔE is nearly zero. It follows then (equation 8.9) that ΔS must be positive. In other words, the entropy of the resting rubber band is greater than that of the stretched state. We are thus led to the conclusion, which could not otherwise have been anticipated, that the molecules in rubber bands possess greater freedom of motion in the resting state than in the stretched. Such a situation could be obtained if the very long molecules from which rubber is made were highly oriented (A in Fig. VIII.7) in the stretched state but more disorganized and randomly arranged in the resting state (B). Freedom of motion would be hampered in (A) because of the essentially crystalline configuration. Consequently (A) would have a lower entropy than (B). From probability considerations, therefore, the transition from stretched to resting state would be favored. Since ΔE is essentially zero, ΔS alone is the determining factor in making ΔG negative for the snap-back.

Turning to a chemical rather than physical transformation, we might examine again one of the processes mentioned earlier in passing (Fig. II.1), the formation of a complex between Cu^{2+} and protein, P:

$$P + Cu^{2+} \rightarrow P-Cu^{2+} \tag{8.13}$$

In this case too the process proceeds spontaneously to the right despite the fact that the internal energy of the complex $P-Cu^{2+}$ is 3 kcal mole^{-1} greater than that of separated P and Cu^{2+} (Fig. VIII.6). Experimental measurements show that ΔS accompanying reaction (8.13) is a large positive number. At first glance such a result would be most surprising, for one would presume that the free components P and Cu^{2+} would have greater freedom of motion than the complex $P-Cu^{2+}$ in which the components are bound together and cannot move about independently. Nevertheless if ΔS is known to be positive, there must be some increase in freedom of motion when reaction (8.13) proceeds to the right. The most likely molecular interpretation of this puzzle draws attention to one feature of the reaction which equation (8.13) does not indicate explicitly—that the participants are all dissolved in aqueous solution. The molecules of

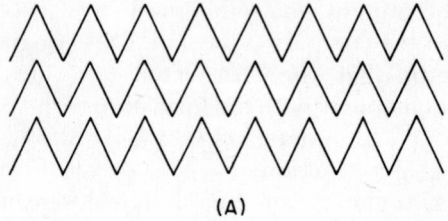

(A)

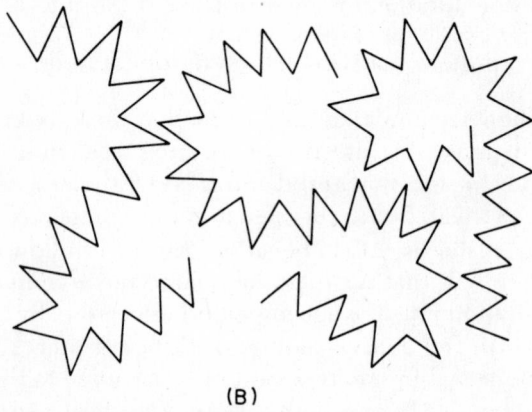

(B)

FIG. VIII.7. Configurations of macromolecules in rubber.

P and Cu^{2+} must be hydrated; that is, water molecules must be bound rigidly to these particles. If, as one would reasonably expect, some of this "frozen" water is released when P and Cu^{2+} combine to form a complex, then more molecules are given increased freedom of motion than are restrained in their movement due to formation of P—Cu^{2+}. Thus in place of equation (8.13) one really should write

$$P(H_2O)_x + Cu(H_2O)_y^{2+} \rightarrow P\text{—}Cu^{2+} + (x+y)H_2O \quad (8.14)$$

where x represents the number of H_2O molecules released by the protein, and y the number released by the copper when the complex is formed. This equation indicates explicitly that "frozen" water molecules are released simultaneously with the formation of the complex, and hence one can understand why the entropy may increase during this reaction.

Finally we might cite another chemical transformation of biological interest, the denaturation of proteins. One of the best examples for thermodynamic analysis is the protein which inhibits the proteolytic enzyme trypsin, called soybean trypsin inhibitor. Thermodynamic data for the denaturation of soybean trypsin inhibitor,

$$\text{protein (native)} \rightarrow \text{protein (denatured)} \quad (8.15)$$

have been accumulated[3] and show that there is an enormous increase in internal energy, 57 kcal mole^{-1}, on formation of the denatured form. Nevertheless, at temperatures near 50°C, the denaturation proceeds spontaneously, that is, ΔG is negative. Again, it follows from equation (8.9) that ΔS must be a large positive number. Denaturation must be accompanied, therefore, by a large increase in freedom of motion of the molecular system. This increased freedom is generally assigned to the protein molecule. In the native state, a protein must be a highly oriented system (e.g., Fig. VIII.8); if in the denatured form it becomes unfolded in part (Fig. VIII.8), it is clear that the freedom of motion within the molecule will be greatly increased. The large positive ΔS thus suggests that the protein molecule becomes disoriented during denaturation.

It is in fact possible to use equation (8.10) to estimate the entropy change to be expected in protein unfolding. We assume that in the native folded form each amino acid residue has a fixed inflexible position. In the unfolded state, each residue that is freed from constraints

[3] M. Kunitz, *J. Gen. Physiol.*, **32**, 257 (1948).

acquires additional possible orientations. Since three interatomic bonds are contributed by each residue in a polypeptide chain we may assume[4] that there are three points of flexibility per residue. If we also assume that at each such point there are two possible orientations (of

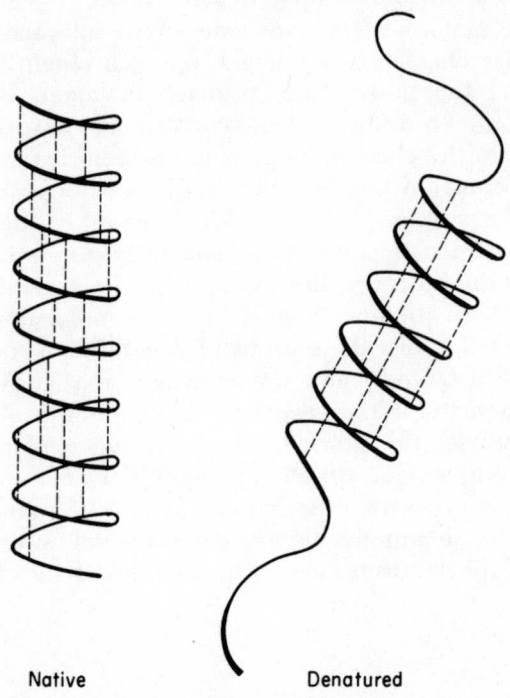

Native   **Denatured**

FIG. VIII.8. A model for protein denaturation.

equal energy) then the total number of new possible orientations contributed by each residue is 2^3. Therefore

$$\Delta S = n(R \ln 2^3) = 4.1n \text{ (cal mole}^{-1} \text{ deg}^{-1}) \quad (8.16)$$

for the "conformational entropy" of unfolding of a pro-

[4] W. Kauzmann *in* "The Mechanism of Enzyme Action," edited by W. D. McElroy and B. Glass, Johns Hopkins Press, Baltimore, 1954, pp. 70–120.

tein molecule of n residues. At 25°C this contributes $-T \Delta S = -1200n$ calories to ΔG for unfolding. This is a large entropic contribution by each residue to the thermodynamic stability of the denatured state. It seems likely that not every residue in the protein is completely freed from constraints upon denaturation.

These examples illustrate some of the information on molecular characteristics which one can obtain from a statistical thermodynamic approach to material transformations. From the molecular-statistical viewpoint, in contrast to the classical approach, one can deduce definite information on the relative freedom of motion of molecular systems. A detailed assignment of this freedom to particular parts of the molecular system is often less certain, however. For example, in the examples described with proteins, highly complex molecules, it is quite possible that the entropy of denaturation is due to changes in bound water rather than to rearrangements in the structural framework of the protein molecule. Nevertheless, the number of alternative explanations available in a given situation is small. Each of them suggests new types of experiments. It is in the ability to interrelate seemingly diverse experimental approaches that the special usefulness of molecular statistics lies.

CONCLUSION

These chapters are an attempt to outline some of the principles of classical and of molecular-statistical energetics. An effort has been made to delineate clearly the axioms of each of these branches of energetics and to show how some of the theorems may be developed from these axioms. Finally, some of the ideas of energetics have been applied to a few biochemical problems to illustrate the types of insight which this branch of science provides for understanding and predicting natural phenomena.

With an introductory discussion of this type, a novice cannot expect to acquire more than a "reading knowledge" of the language. For those interested in extending their proficiency in the field of energetics, some of the following books may prove helpful.

Classical energetics

Guggenheim, E. A., "Modern Thermodynamics." Methuen, London, 1933.

Klotz, I. M., "Chemical Thermodynamics." Benjamin, New York, 1964.

Lewis, G. N., and Randall, M., "Thermodynamics." (revised by K. S. Pitzer and L. Brewer). McGraw-Hill, New York, 1961.

Wall, F. T., "Chemical Thermodynamics." Freeman, San Francisco, 1965.

Statistical energetics

Andrews, F. C., "Equilibrium Statistical Mechanics." Wiley, New York, 1963.

Davidson, N., "Statistical Mechanics." McGraw-Hill, New York, 1962.

Dole, M., "Introduction to Statistical Thermodynamics." Prentice-Hall, Englewood Cliffs, New Jersey, 1954.

Guggenheim, E. A., "Boltzmann's Distribution Law." (Interscience), New York, 1955.

Hill, T. L., "An Introduction to Statistical Thermodynamics." Addison-Wesley, Reading, Massachusetts, 1960.

Irreversible Processes

DeGroot, S. R., "Thermodynamics of Irreversible Processes." Wiley (Interscience), New York, 1951.

Denbigh, K. G., "The Thermodynamics of the Steady State." Methuen, London, 1962.

Fitts, D. D., "Nonequilibrium Thermodynamics." McGraw-Hill, New York, 1962.

Prigogine, I., "Introduction to Thermodynamics of Irreversible Processes." Thomas, Springfield, Illinois, 1955.

Information Theory

Brillouin, L., "Scientific Uncertainty and Information." Academic Press, New York, 1964.